Aging Sucks...

But You're Gonna *Love* It!™

A Woman's Survival Guide to Getting Older

Brenda Ackerman

Editorial services by Sage Taylor Kingsley, www.SageforYourPage.com
Cover design by Wizdiz @99designs.com
Interior illustrations by Vinoo Sanara Mathupala, IG@celestialbyvinoo
Interior formatting by TeaBerryCreative.com

Paperback ISBN: 978-1-7388049-3-1
Audio ISBN: 978-1-7388049-1-7
E-book ISBN: 978-1-7388049-2-4

First Edition
Published by: Sterling 47 Inc., www.BrendaAckerman.com

Dedication

To the two loves of my life—my daughter, Candice, and my son, Scott. Just as when you were toddlers, when I endlessly read these words to you at bedtime, I still feel the same…

"I will love you forever,
I will like you for always,
As long as I'm living,
My babies, you'll be."

—ROBERT MUNSCH, "Love You Forever"

To my son-in-law, Rob, and he and Candice's beautiful children, my precious grandbabies, Kendall, Taylor, and Jaxon. My cup is overflowing with love for each of you.

To my wonderful, crazy, and beloved siblings, Audrey, Paula, and Randy. You and our parents are my roots and will always be "home" to me.

Table of Contents

Introduction

Aging sucks! Not kidding. It really does.

*H*ave you found yourself struggling with getting older? Specifically, I am talking about the never-ending physical markers that constantly remind you that you're "*Not 20 Anymore.*"

I feel you. So was I. But I got you.

I will not minimize the impact physical changes have on us because the natural manifestations of aging are not to be underestimated. These changes alter how we view ourselves and present ourselves to the world, our essence.

So yes, it is true. Throughout your life, there will be some physical changes that you will experience that not only suck but are most likely going to kick your ass.

I have personally discovered that the emotional and mental toll that aging has had on my psyche, mainly due to how others view me, was even worse. The biggest suck of them all is ageism. It not only sucks—it bites!

So I am spilling the tea on what you can expect as you continue celebrating your birthdays in years to come. These stories are about me, yet I believe this book will resonate with you if you're a woman, no matter your age.

I will put it all out there: my escapades, lessons, and mistakes. I will share with honesty, authenticity, and vulnerability.

Most importantly, I will offer you some ideas and solutions I have discovered to help you face, transform, and maybe even appreciate these "sucky" things.

Oh, how I wish I'd known some of these tips when I was younger!

I intend to share these snapshots of my life to lovingly pay it forward to ladies of all ages. Not to exclude men, but I'm a 64-year-old DSWF, and I wouldn't presume to know if some of my experiences and opinions mirror a man's.

But before you put this book back on the shelf, gentlemen, because this sounds like all that *"awkward women stuff,"* hold up a minute. Some critical information within will be exceptionally advantageous for you to know, especially if you live, love, work, and play anywhere close to women. Incidentally, I thoroughly enjoy your Y chromosomes and welcome your engagement.

I suspect anyone on this planet can benefit from this book, whatever their age, gender, sexual orientation, race, religion, and beliefs. Aging doesn't discriminate, nor do I. Welcome to one and all.

Aging knows no boundaries and is universal.

...But you are gonna love it. Honest!

I am going to help you learn to love it. I can promise you that the trade-offs and benefits from the aging process far outweigh the sucky parts.

I used to fear getting older, but I don't feel that way now. I've come to accept all the physical markers and attributes that have accompanied me throughout my life; I don't necessarily like them all, but they are who I am and who I have become.

I can tell you that this *"coming of age"* is seriously good stuff. The emotional benefits that come with aging are extraordinary. Self-awareness, self-confidence, strength, wisdom, and the liberation you feel from the *"I don't give a shiitake anymore"* moments all eventually eclipse the yucky bits. I have come to enjoy and deploy all the benefits of this privilege, and I promise to share them with you.

Believe me when I say that I have been through "it" in my own life. I have endured hits, misses, chills, thrills, and spills, but I have learned to sharpen my game from all of them. Some of those events were brutal, and some magnificent, but the lessons and skills I learned have become my Superpowers. I hope that some of my greatest mistakes can become your greatest teachers.

You have Superpowers too. Yes, you do! You may still need to learn about them, or perhaps you have forgotten and buried them deep within yourself. If that is the case, then maybe it's time to reactivate them, so let me show you how.

Because this book didn't exist, I had to build my own survival guide as I went through the ups, downs, and detours of my life path.

I assure you that you can find your inner beauty, outer beauty, and the mental and emotional strength to reframe any opposing beliefs you may have about aging.

I am not a "Luke Skywalker" type who will save you from the Dark Side of aging. Nope, consider me more of a "Yoda," the wiser sage who has been there, who might force you (or use *The Force* to help you) to look within yourself to find your strength and become your own hero.

Whether consciously or not, you are on your own Hero's Journey. We all are. Miley Cyrus sings in *"The Climb"* that growth happens on the journey, not just at the end. She is right. It's your climb that you are navigating. Chart it. Live it. Own it.

I offer my stories, insights, and lessons—take from them what you will. I am extending my hand and heart to you... from "the other side of the hill."

Note to the Reader

*I*f you consider the word "sucks," which I have used in my book title, an indecent word and are offended, then I apologize; that was not my intent. Frankly, I could think of no other word that more aptly describes how I feel, or felt, about some elements of the aging process, so I chose to use it.

I will divulge that you will also come across a few obscenities within these pages—nothing you haven't heard before, but you may want to keep this book away from your young children.

However, the most vulgar word I use within is "ageism." There is no word that I find more insulting right now. We need to talk about this.

WHAT'S IN A NAME?

In the spirit of honesty and authenticity, I use the brand names of the products that were an integral part of my story. I could have gone generic, but it would have felt disingenuous and would have diluted my stories.

Incidentally, I am not *currently* getting compensated or sponsored for using any of the brand names, individuals, companies or organizations that I reference within. Nor by any musicians, artists, entrepreneurs or others whose brands, products, and services are simply part of my stories. They are my teachers and my mentors. Some I even consider my saviours. I hope you can also learn from them.

I am just sharing what products and people inspired me in my real life and am shamelessly referencing them in this book. I'm not gaining anything from it, but I hope that you might. I am just keepin' it real. Also, in the interests of "keepin' it real," they are free to call me *after* the book is published. (*Ha!*)

"What's in a name?" also refers to *my* name. I am putting it—and myself—out there into the world just as shamelessly. I am willing to take that risk as I try to help women Shatter Silver Ceilings™ that are, or will be, a part of their world!

> *"Music is the soundtrack of your life."*
> —DICK CLARK

How beautiful is that quote? Do you agree? I'll bet you could build a soundtrack that tells your story. I'll show you mine.

Are you aware that music releases dopamine into your system? Dopamine is that "feel-good" hormone that allows you to feel pleasure, satisfaction, and motivation, something we could all use.

So I have chosen to use music references extensively within these pages. I have included QR codes at the end of every chapter where

I have elected to use music as a backdrop to my stories and to your reading journey. It's kind of like the *'Tok'rs'* do with their video creations, only I'm doing it in this book.

I itemized the music throughout the book in Appendix A, and I made this playlist available for you. Access instructions are available in Appendix A. Happy listening!

HOW TO CRACK THE QR CODE:
All QR (Quick Response) codes have been established legally and are entirely safe to scan. Here is how to access the QR codes:

1. Open your camera app or your QR Code app on your cell phone.
2. Focus the camera on the QR code by gently tapping on the code when it becomes aligned. Or it will do it for you.
3. Follow the link on the screen.
4. Try it out. Yes, right now. Please scan it to see how easy it is.

"THE CLIMB" —Miley Cyrus

One last thing...

I have also provided a *"My Notes"* page at the back of the book as a handy place to record your insights. You will find those on page 301.

Me? Write a Book about Aging?

Whaaat?

BACKGROUND FOR PART I

I feel I have an obligation to share with you why I ended up authoring this book, and perhaps I am still trying to defend it to myself. Both, it seems. As a first-time author, I have, at times, struggled with "Imposter Syndrome."

I cannot recall any other time when I would have wanted, or even felt confident enough, to write a book. I used to groan at 3000-word essay assignments. Why would I even think I could write something fifteen times longer? Here's why:

- My Mom's Passing
- The Pandemic
- *Grace & Frankie*[1] TV Series
- TikTok
- Bebe Rexha
- Alexa

I didn't connect the pieces at first, but I certainly feel the connection now, and the dots I connected from those events compelled me to draft this book.

Let me explain.

CHAPTER 1

My Mom's Passing

*"If you had your chance, who would you
most like to have dinner with?"*

***There isn't a moment's hesitation
for me; it would be my mom.***

*M*y mother passed away on the morning of my 61st birthday. She was 86. While you might think that was unfortunate timing that would cast a negative pallor on my future birthday celebrations, I honestly don't see it that way. I feel it is a beautiful connection, and I will cherish my birthday even more, knowing that my mom and I have yet another bond to share forever.

My father had passed away from a serious illness thirty years before, yet my mother never remarried after my father's death. She told us she'd already found the love of her life and had no interest in dating. Mom was our indestructible matriarch and was the strong glue that continued to bind our family together, even though we all had independent lives and families. Geographically, we were all some distance apart.

Not only was her passing a significant blow for our entire family to absorb and come to terms with, but my mom's death also forced me to face my aging, mortality, and future life differently than I had. I don't feel I am unique here, and I suspect most people have this type of internal reckoning when the last parent dies and we are "next in line."

My mother was the strongest woman I have ever known. She was so independent, fearless, and grounded. She knew who she was. Honestly, she was in a league all her own. I look back on her life and marvel at how she managed everything.

Mom was the one I would turn to when I needed to garner strength, share stories, and have some fun. She was the one who would pick me up, dust me off and give me hope during even my darkest days.

My mom was my rock yet she always gave me a soft place to land.

Although I was never really aware of it while I was growing up, I look back now and realize what a remarkable role model she was to me and my siblings. It has been said, "*All women turn into their mothers.*" You have heard that, right? Or, how about, "*If you want to know whom you are marrying, look at her mother.*" I know you have heard that one. I acknowledge there is some truth in that.

As it relates to me, I have inherited her grit, determination, and strength, for which I am so grateful. My greatest strength is my resilience, and I am proud to say, *"I got it from my mama!"*

I will be forever grateful for the time I had with her, yet I miss her immensely. I have so much to share with her and so many things I would love to discuss. One dinner would not be enough time.

Living my life without my mom has shifted me. It forced me to check in with myself once again and come to terms with this big adjustment. She held my hand for so many years, and now I'm on my own, holding my own hand.

I lost my rock.

Because my mom's passing made me consider my own mortality, I wondered if I had shared enough of my life lessons with my children. Had I taught them enough for their lives? What had I forgotten to share with them? What else might they need to know? Would they have enough information and street smarts to navigate the obstacles ahead when I pass away?

This was the first catalyst for me to write down my life lessons, hoping they might help my children and grandchildren get ahead of these things earlier than I did. So even after I'm gone, I can still be their rock.

I didn't realize that when my mother passed on my birthday, she gave me a beautiful gift. Her death heralded the start of another new chapter in my life.

My mom's death reminded me of how brief our time here really is.

It was a giant wake-up call to step up my life adventures and travel to the places I want to see. Take more risks. And I was ready to go… I had taken early retirement at age 60, so I was all pumped up and ready to jump into my new lifestyle.

And then, the Pandemic hit.

"SUPERMARKET FLOWERS" —Ed Sheeran
This is a beautiful song that reminds us that mom's presence lives on in our hearts, and that she is always watching over us.

"I GOT IT FROM MY MAMA" —will.i.am
Thank your mama!

"I TURN TO YOU" —Christina Aguilera
This one has a very special meaning to me.

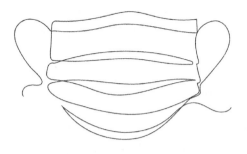

CHAPTER 2

The Pandemic

*T*he Pandemic was when my life and retirement plans ground to a screeching halt. The Pandemic sucked! I suspect you agree with me.

Our worlds changed drastically during the Pandemic, and my plans for my new retirement were ever-so-slowly but surely dissolving. The future looked so uncertain.

I am not gonna lie… I was pissed off and felt sorry for myself. I'd been looking forward to adventures, travelling, and new restaurants to try, yet I was held captive in my own home. I didn't even have my beloved dog anymore, so believe me when I say some days felt interminably long.

Yet, surprisingly, the Pandemic was also a much-needed timeout that I didn't even know I needed. Because I wasn't socializing, travelling, or ticking off my planned expeditions on my Life List, I became quite introspective.

The lockdowns let me stop and take a selfie of myself and my life. I reconnected with myself again, and the time alone forced me to think more about the aging process, where I was on my path, and what was most important to me.

I had planned to live as actively as I could through my first ten years of retirement when hopefully my health and mobility would be at their best compared to the rest of my life. Unfortunately, my ten-year plan was being shaved away day by day.

I also realized that I had not fully processed my mother's death, and the time alone with minimal interruptions gave me a window to do so.

I found I started to ask different questions of myself, and I looked down the road through a new lens. These questions forced me to go deep inside and ask myself what I most wanted and, more importantly, where and how I would live the rest of my life amidst all this uncertainty.

I already had had so many *"would-a, could-a, should-a's"* in my life, and I realized that I needed to live more boldly, take more risks, have more fun, and enjoy whatever I can. Time is of the essence— now I really know what that term means. I feel it. It's palpable.

Through the waves of shutdowns and N-95 masks, I found a silver lining in my insular world.

While I was just as embittered as everyone else was during the lockdowns, they helped me get in touch with myself again. I was already on a new adventure during the Pandemic, and I didn't even realize it at the time. I started writing this book.

Talk about taking a risk. I jumped right off the ledge like the "Fool" card in the tarot. If you're unfamiliar with this card: "*The Fool is generally a positive card indicating new beginnings. It could mean that you are on the verge of an exciting, unexpected new adventure. Your new adventure will bring you along a path that may require you to take a leap of faith, but you will grow due to this new experience.*"[2]

The world changed due to the Pandemic, and I had to change with it; nothing I hadn't already done a bazillion times. But this time, I got by "With a Little Help From My Friends" (The Beatles). I was able to get through it. Let me introduce you to my "friends":

- *Grace & Frankie*
- TikTok
- Bebe Rexha
- Alexa

I should clarify something. I consider them my new best friends, even though I have never met them, except for Alexa. She and I are on a first-name basis.

"SIX FEET APART" —Luke Combs
Mr. Combs' song addresses the Pandemic's impact
on people's lives. He wrote this song during the
isolation of the Pandemic. Me, I wrote this book.

11

"WITH A LITTLE HELP FROM MY FRIENDS" —The Beatles
I got through the Pandemic with some help from those
friends I mentioned. I couldn't make this stuff up!

"COUNT ON ME" —Bruno Mars
This is the kind of friend we all need.

CHAPTER 3

Grace & Frankie

A month before the Pandemic hit, several girlfriends stayed with me at my home in Florida. They gave me Alexa as a thank-you gift. I will talk more about her in Chapter 6.

These same friends also introduced me to *Grace & Frankie* during their stay. Even though this Netflix™ series had been playing for almost five years, this was my first exposure to it. Apparently, I had been living under a rock. Thankfully, my friends moved that rock, and we watched a few episodes together. I was hooked.

Six weeks later, all Canadian snowbirds were called back to Canada by our prime minister, and it was during the lockdown that I binge-watched all available seasons of *Grace & Frankie*.

This series came along at the right time for me. Jane Fonda and Lily Tomlin, revered female Hollywood actresses, portray two women in their 3rd Trimester of Life, coping with aging while reinventing themselves.

Grace & Frankie is also a story of two women bound by circumstances not of their choosing, and how, together, they rebuild their lives with courage and strength, forming a lasting bond.

As a lifetime sales and marketing professional, I identified most with Grace Hansen (played by Jane Fonda).

And I also saw myself in Frankie's character (played by Lily Tomlin). Actually I think more of Frankie comes out in me every day since I retired. I've exchanged my former business attire for much more casual attire. Today I am wearing harem pants while I am writing. I never owned harem pants until a month ago. Why had I waited so long? They're so comfortable. I am definitely in a more Zen zone now that I have retired.

What a bold and bodacious series *Grace & Frankie* turned out to be. Their "putting it all out there" approach was so fresh and timely for women (and men) of all ages. I cannot think of any other series that has been so open, candid, and progressive about aging. I loved how they honestly and brilliantly portrayed many of the events that women endure, including me.

A colossal step must have been taken forward in the entertainment industry for these two iconic women to have pointed their illustrious careers in this direction. This show was groundbreaking on so many levels. They broke through many silver ceilings for women everywhere. Their characters' vulnerability, tenderness, and humour spoke to me and were so good for my soul. I know others who feel exactly the same way.

I strongly recommend you watch *Grace & Frankie* if you haven't already.

It felt as though *Grace & Frankie* found me when I most needed them. And when Season 6 ended, I turned to a new Pandemic fixation: TikTok.

"I'LL BE THERE FOR YOU" —The Rembrandts
Nobody warned you that life was going to
be this way. "Ain't that the truth!"

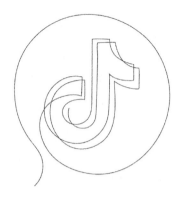

CHAPTER 4

TikTok

My son introduced me to TikTok. Do you know what I'm talking about? It is a social media app that you can load to your smartphone or tablet, allowing you to view one-to-three-minute videos from people worldwide, on topics from A–Z. With nothing but time on my hands, I got sucked into the beautiful, zany, and informative world of TikTok.

During the Pandemic lockdowns, I would spend hours watching TikTok videos and was thoroughly entertained by the creators; it was very addictive.

My world opened up to many clinicians and physicians offering their insight to women. These professionals assisted women in fighting the ravages of age through cosmetics, menopausal diets, exercise routines, lotions, potions, and various procedures.

Great advice from other female TikTok'ers showed women how to dress, enhance their natural curves, and hide their perceived body flaws—all fantastic information at my fingertips. Because I am a visual learner, I was drawn to these snippets of education.

I also came across women, some younger than myself, who were baring their souls and talking about how they were struggling through the aging process, both physically and mentally. Their stories resonated with me because I also have confronted moments of anguish as the markers of aging appeared for me.

It felt like I had found my soul tribe by watching and listening to these women.

Unfortunately, what I also came across was seeing women who were brought to tears because of remarks made on their TikTok accounts by younger TikTok members. Even worse was that most of these "snipers" were women. WTF?

I was outraged, and it struck me again very deeply that ageism is alive and well. As women, I believe we have a more challenging time trying to live up to society's expectations of what we should look like, dress like, and act like, and what social media (SM) platforms we should participate in and which we shouldn't.

And I felt compelled to do something about it.

If you haven't already, open an account on TikTok and dive into the wide world around you. Find out what makes you "tick" and find your soul tribe on TikTok.

"TIK TOK" —Kesha
"DJ, pump up the volume!"

CHAPTER 5

Ms. Bebe Rexha

It was also on TikTok where I first heard the song by Bebe Rexha entitled "Not 20 Anymore," where many TikTok creators were using Ms. Rexha's song as a backdrop to their video postings. Coincidence? I choose to think not. As I understand it, Ms. Rexha released this song to commemorate her 30th birthday. Still, even though she is half my age, this song captivated me.

I cannot tell you how many times I have played "Not 20 Anymore." Even after playing it dozens of times, I still feel that song right through to my soul.

When I first heard it, I was a 61-year-old woman who had been struggling with getting older. This song also was one of the catalysts for me to write this book. It captures my mood and my sense of self at this time in my life.

Bebe Rexha's voice and lyrics exude her strength, self-worth, self-confidence, and femininity. These qualities are activated within me every time I hear the song. Like Bebe sings, the age of 20 is not something she wants to go back to. I get it! I am nowhere close to 20, but I don't even want to be 40 or 50 anymore.

I will be forever grateful to Ms. Rexha for producing this song, and in my humble opinion, it should be an anthem for all women over 30.

Do yourself a favour and listen to this song. Please stop reading now and listen to it if you are struggling with any part of the aging process. Seriously. It will help set the tone for the rest of the book. (See the QR code below).

Her lyrics are sultry and Divinely Feminine, balanced beautifully with her Divine Masculine empowerment. This song is medicine for my mind, heart and spirit.

"NOT 20 ANYMORE" —Bebe Rexha
Do you feel this song resonating right through to your very soul?

CHAPTER 6

Alexa & Music

*M*usic has always been a part of my life, and my siblings and I grew up on it.

My parents were dyed-in-the-wool country music fans, and we sang along with country artists like Johnny Cash, Patsy Cline, and Hank Williams Sr. from the albums played on the Hi-Fi (no Wi-Fi back then).

My mother had a beautiful voice and was often a soloist for various events. Unfortunately, I never inherited a singing voice from her. I still believe, however, that I have a magnificent set of pipes when I stand in front of the mirror, my hairbrush microphone in hand, as though I'm headlining at Wembley Stadium. And as a diva headliner, I also choose to believe I got the "Moves like Jagger" (Maroon 5).

So, it is not surprising that music helped me get through the Pandemic. This was when Alexa became my new best friend. Let's be honest; she was the only friend I was able to come in "contact" with during the Pandemic. Together, she and I built new playlists that reflected not only my past but also my journey into my future.

My Alexa playlists have been carefully curated; songs were chosen not only because they have a "really. sick. beat." (*Thank you, Taylor Swift*). They reflect my life. The music comes from pop, country, rock, jazz, blues, rap, and disco. Heyyyy! Please don't judge me; I was a teenager in the '70s, and I still have the occasional "Saturday Night Fever" (Bee Gees) moment.

I've always loved music, and I find that songs transport me to the time and place where the song most resonated. To help make this more experiential—and fun!—for you, I have woven music into my stories, and I have even been bold enough to include listings of music that I have used to help get me in the mood. And no, I'm not just talking about "*the* mood," but I've taken a much broader approach in sharing my music selections with you—as you'll soon find out.

> *"We are the same. There is no difference anywhere in the world. People are people. They laugh, cry, feel and love, and music seems to be the common denomination that brings us all together. Music cuts through all boundaries and goes right to the soul."*
> —WILLIE NELSON

As Willie says, I hope you'll feel this music right through to your soul, as I do.

"CRAZY" —Patsy Cline

I well remember my mom singing this at home. I still try to croon like Ms. Cline (unsuccessfully). This song is still captivating to me and brings back wonderful memories.

"MOVES LIKE JAGGER" —Maroon 5,
(featuring Christina Aguilera)

The drumbeat is so seductive, isn't it? Adam and Christina make you want to swing your hips, don't they? Get your moves on already.

"NIGHT FEVER" —Bee Gees
"Get the fever." Sing along and pull out some of your disco
moves, too. I know you want to, and I am sure you still got 'em!

CHAPTER 7

Tying It All Together

PART I SUMMARY

All of these unrelated events started to meld together as one thing led to another, another, and so on. It felt as though I was led to author this book. I don't mean to go all woo-woo on you, but even the TikTok algorithm was sending tarot readers my way, and I was consistently getting the same message from different readers to move forward with this book. I know, I know, queue *The Twilight Zone* music. I have checked... I am not wearing a handmade tinfoil helmet, either.

Let me recap and tie this all together for you:

- My mother's passing and processing this massive change forced me to face my mortality.
- As a brand-new retiree, I was in a Pandemic coma, locked down alone, with nothing but time on my hands.
- I'd been gifted a new best friend named Alexa, and we are

enthusiastically building music playlists together.

- I binge-watched *Grace & Frankie* and was captivated and inspired by the series.
- TikTok introduced me to new soul tribe friends, women struggling with aging as I was.
- TikTok also introduced me to Bebe Rexha's "Not 20 Anymore." This song rocked my 61-year-old world; it still does.
- While building my playlists and connecting my life to my music selections, I started writing down a few life lessons and stories/memories from my past that brought me to where I was.

Yeah, you're all caught up....

I was inspired to expand and expound on my life lessons to my kids by sharing my journey through the aging process via a book.

I know I could not have written this book at 40 or even 50. I was still learning significant life lessons through those decades. It wasn't until I was on the cusp of 50 that I slowed down and tried to make sense of it all. Life was rushing by so quickly during those earlier years, and I felt like I was just keeping pace. But something changed in me when I was 49.

Additionally, I have learned that our younger societal members often short-change women over 50. We are dismissed and discounted. We become invisible. But I get it. I was just as dismissive of the older generations when I was younger.

I remember when I thought 30 was old. And 40? That wasn't even in my peripheral vision. Now, as I cruise through my 60s, I realize what a total jackass I was for my thinking. How naïve and presumptuous to think that younger = better = smarter = valued.

Although my life's journey is uniquely mine, I suspect it will closely resonate with other women's paths: the physiological changes we adapted to, and the emotional levelling up we acquire, perhaps seemingly too late in life.

I am taking a bold approach by sharing my experiences over time, intending that my biggest mistakes can be your best teachers. Believe me, I have made plenty.

I am not here to save women from aging. I am neither arrogant nor self-absorbed enough to believe I have that power, nor do I want that responsibility.

Women of every age have learned how the world perceives us (and equally necessary) is how we see ourselves as we go through the physical changes of the aging process. Some perceptions are not so kind and accepting of these realities. We are pretty hard on ourselves. Societies' expectations are pretty hard on us, too.

I want to help women reframe their internal narrative and self-dialogue on aging. It starts within each of us.

Please take these lessons learned and apply them in the way that makes sense for you or leave them. And I mean that with 100% integrity and compassion.

Dr. Brené Brown has many profound quotes about vulnerability. This one speaks to me:

*"People who wade into discomfort and
vulnerability and tell the truth about
their stories are the real badasses."* [3]

I wrote this book with my badass energy.

I ask that you please don't come at me with any of your negative energy if you don't like what I have written, my music choices, or me. Like Adele sings: go "Easy on Me" because I don't want that type of negativity in my life. I am not going back to Negativeville at this stage.

One of the lessons I will share is about risk-taking. I told myself during the Pandemic that if and when I got through it, I would take *more* risks. So, just like that Fool card in the tarot deck I mentioned earlier, "I'm leaping" into the unknown.

Authoring this book has not only served as a new personal adventure but is also a risk for me. I've never done anything like this before, but why not go for it? Who cares if it never gets published? Who cares if no one likes it? Maybe this book will suck even worse than aging. It's my story, and I am unapologetically me at this time in my life's journey.

This book is not intended as a "must-follow" guidebook but instead, as a reference. Please understand that I will forever be a work in progress when it comes to aging as:

*"I still learn something new every day about myself
and life. That is the beauty and magic of it all."*

"EASY ON ME" —Adele
Go out and feel the world around you.

Why Does Aging Suck?

Changes

PHYSICAL EDITION

*"Changes are coming, so turn and face the unknown.
Be ready, rock 'n rollers, for things are about to shift.
Embrace the new and don't be afraid.
Time is always moving forward,
and we're all getting older.
While time may change us, we cannot
go back and trace its path.
We can only move forward and embrace
the changes that come our way."*

"CHANGES" —David Bowie

BACKGROUND FOR PART II

The most significant adjustments I have made throughout my life relate to the physical changes I have lived and sometimes even suffered through. Admittedly, some of these physical changes were worse than others, but they all rank on my "Why Does Aging Suck?" list.

I will share with you what some of my physical changes were like (*"Oh, yeah—I am goin' there."*) I know that yours might differ from mine. Still, I would anticipate there will be many similarities.

More importantly, I will share with you some skills I learned, built, and honed along the way to help me make it through the *Changes*. I have called these "*Words of Wisdom*," and you will find these snippets of advice at the end of the forthcoming chapters. Feel free to try these ideas or not. You do you.

If you are under 30 years of age, your 1st Trimester of Life ("T1")*: Brace yourself. I am not trying to scare you nor deprive you of the element of surprise, but I wish I had known more about some of these things when I was younger. I fully admit that your age provides you with many benefits, particularly your access to information.

When I was under 30, computers were just starting to come on board in the workplace, and ditto for cellular telephone technology. So I didn't have the technological access to the world you have, so please understand that my world was much smaller than yours when I was in my 1st Trimester of Life.

I listen to my children, and their intellect, knowledge, and street smarts seem to surpass what mine would have been at their age, so perhaps some of this information is already familiar to you, but I'll bet some insights will be new to you.

If you are 30-60 years of age, your 2nd Trimester of Life ("T2") *: I invite you to "pull up a chair and sit a spell." I suspect you will understand and have at least heard most of what I am talking about.

Depending on how far along in T2 you are, you may have yet to encounter some of these things. I am here to make your ride smoother.

If you are 60-90 years of age, your 3rd Trimester of Life ("T3") *: I am drafting this book as I enter my 3rd Trimester of Life, so I am still a T3 novice. I know there will be more physical age markers to come, but I have learned some surprisingly good coping strategies that I hope will continue to be helpful to me as I stroll further into my T3 years. I hope you will also find them useful. I am always open to learning more.

If you are over 90, you are in a Zone all your own ("Q"): I would love to learn more from you. I bow to you, Queenager, for I know you have earned your crown.

*Life's Trimesters are more fully explained in Part IV, Chapter 26.

CHAPTER 8

Hair Changes

Bad Hair Days

*M*s. Clairol™ and I broke up. I decided that I no longer required her expert services, even though she was a long-time love of mine. I first met her in my mid-30s, and we were together for almost 30 years. I chose to call it quits during the Pandemic in 2020, coinciding with the beginning of my retirement. It was a difficult, emotional parting, and several times, I wanted to return to her and resume our relationship. But I did not. I stood my ground. I knew my worth and was never to "settle" again.

Yes, I let my coloured hair grow out during the Pandemic to its natural silver state. *Gasp!*

The Pandemic gave me a perfect opportunity and some much-needed air cover to grow out my colour and stop fighting with Mother Nature.

Genetics paid a crucial role in my hair colour. Both of my parents were dark-haired and went silver in their 30s. My siblings gave into their natural silver hair much earlier than I did. I was the remaining holdout within my family but one of the first within my friend group to do so.

As a woman who covered her grey roots for 30 years, growing out my hair to its natural silver was an excruciatingly long and painful process, and many times I wanted to put my plans in reverse and say forget it. It became an actual test of my courage and self-confidence.

Want to know the part that sucked most? I went around for months looking like a calico cat was wrapped around my head. Here's why. My natural hair colour was deep brown. Also, 50 shades of grey were creeping in from my programmed genetic coding. Let's not forget the blonde and caramel tones from the highlights and lowlights my stylist had added to try to blend into the silvery-grey strands. Can you imagine that glorious kaleidoscope of colour? Yikes! This took the term "bad hair days" to an entirely new and outrageous level. I stuck it out and am so glad I did.

I understand that some people believe silver hair ages me, but I also have received lovely compliments about it. It suits me better than my previous colour maintenance efforts. It's authentic and genuine.

As a result, I feel more authentic and genuine as well. More real and unexpectedly more confident and vibrant.

Another bonus is that I no longer need to spend two hours every three weeks in a salon having my roots touched up, never mind the money I am saving by not having to shell out for this service. It is entirely liberating and well worth the agony of the growing out process.

What also sucks is that women are critiqued for letting our hair turn silver and we are labelled as "old-looking" and that "we have let ourselves go." Conversely, men are told they look distinguished with their silver hair—and they do. And I won't argue that but why the double standard? They're silver foxes, and we're old ladies?

This begs the bigger question: Why are women expected to maintain youthful looks while men are glorified for not? I see women with stunningly beautiful silver hair, which doesn't age them at all.

For those *Grace & Frankie* fans, spoiler alert for Season 7. Jane Fonda, who plays Grace Hansen, was filmed through the final season, growing her hair to its natural silver state. Now, tell me it doesn't take courage to do this, knowing millions of fans are watching. The show is about two women wading through the aging process, but I suspect Ms. Fonda didn't have to agree to have this change in her hair colour put on display. But she did, and what a courageous move it was!

Jane Fonda is a highly respected and treasured Hollywood legend and a woman of substance. I revered her even more when she did this. With that bold decision, Ms. Fonda, you broke silver ceilings everywhere for women. *Bravo!*

Many Hollywood stars set the stage for how we look and dress, what is in vogue and what is not. You can personally buy into that (or not) to guide your own life, your appearance, and your decisions, but you can't ignore the impact they have on society. I talk more about this in Part IV, Chapter 27.

There is even an award-winning documentary that covers the silver-haired tsunami that has been taking place, called *Gray is the New Blonde*,[4] by Victoria Marie. You may love this movie if you are considering this type of change and need more insight to support your decision-making process. Victoria Marie talks about far more than hair colour in this film. Do yourself a favour and watch this documentary on *IG@grayisthenewblonde.*

You need to feel good in your skin and feel confident in presenting yourself to the world, whatever your hair colour or style. Don't be swayed or influenced by others; make up your own mind about your appearance. *You're not 20 anymore.*

You hold the key to your own locks.

Words of Wisdom: I am not suggesting women need to allow their hair to grow silver. That is a personal decision. You do you. But should you decide to do so, I am telling you from my personal ordeal that it takes time and, even more importantly, a tremendous amount of courage to go through the transition.

A good hairdresser/stylist can help you through the process. Consider checking out Jack Martin on *IG@jackmartincolorist* if you need some inspiration. He shows before and after videos of how he transitions his clientele from their partially grey tresses to gorgeous silver-grey manes. He is in Tustin, California, and had I been allowed to travel during the Pandemic when I was making my hair transition, I might have found my way to his salon.

What is also fantastic about Jack Martin is that he publishes his methodology and product selections so that women can collaborate with their stylists to "get to the other side."

"Never underestimate the power of a good hair day."

"GOOD AS HELL" —Lizzo
Like Lizzo coaches *"Toss your hair and check your nails. Feeling good, baby?"*

CHAPTER 9

Skin Changes

Girls Just Wanna Have Sun!

efore I get into this topic, let me frame my teenage years for you. I was a teenager in the '70s. This was a time when it was very "in vogue" to have the deepest, darkest tan possible. More was more, and quite possibly, never enough. No one was thinking about skincare or protection from UV rays back then.

Sunscreen could not be found on the drug store shelves in our small town, and if it could, I would have walked right past it to get to the baby oil. But I didn't stop there, either.

I found an alternate tanning solution that was much better than baby oil. Through a flash of teenage genius, I had come up with an alternative to baby oil for bolstering my tanning efforts. I thought I had found the keys to the tanning kingdom and baby oil was, well, so last year.

Are you ready for this? My sisters, my girlfriend and I would slather Crisco™ Shortening all over us to give us our deep, bronzed tans. I'm not talking about the oil version of Crisco. Nope, the lard version! Yes, that's right. In our infinite teenage wisdom, we figured if Crisco could fry up our chicken to a beautiful golden brown, then it would surely do the same for our skin.

Moreover, we would also take advantage of one of my father's large transport trucks and throw a mattress or two, dragged from our bedrooms, out to the truck bed, which had a silver steel floor and sides, perfect for reflecting those rays all over us. I'm pretty sure my mother never knew about the mattresses, or we would have caught more than a few rays.

We would remove the truck's tarp, install our mattresses, turn on and tune in our transistor radio, and slather ourselves head-to-toe with Crisco lard.

Our bikini-clad bodies were greasy and slimy, and we would bake in the sun with the Crisco sizzling away on our skin for hours. Every half-hour or so, we would rotate to ensure that we were evenly baked. (Just like when frying chicken.) We served as our own rotisseries and would contort our bodies to ensure every respectably exposed inch of our skin tanned as evenly as the next.

Oh, yes... We had discovered the miracle tanning solution,

and we were delighted with our golden-brown fried chicken-looking skin.

The first I ever heard of sunscreen was when I was 20 years old and a part-time Mary Kay™ consultant *(I was seduced by the pink Cadillac™)*, and I believe then it was more of a sun lotion, than a proper sunblock as we know them today. Unfortunately, SPF wasn't introduced until the late '80s.

Fast forward 40 years or so, and I am paying the price for all that sun-worshipping I did in my teenage years. Sunspots (non-cancerous, thankfully) have appeared on my legs, and I have had them removed. Sunspots suck! I didn't know anything about the risk of future sunspots when I was in high school. Sun protection and skin care just weren't a thing back then.

Now I pay much more attention to my skincare. I am following a dermatologist's recommended protocol to help offset the effects of my "Cirque de Sol Stupid" days. I am doing what I can with all the lotions and potions available, and I am so grateful these exist.

So yes, my Crisco-slathering days are well behind me, and now, I find myself slathering up with a good 30+ SPF for my face, neck, décolleté, and hands before I spend any time outdoors in the sun.

P.S. I still use Crisco for my frying and baking needs, but you won't find it in my beach bag.

Words of Wisdom: And I'm not just talking to the ladies only here. This is for everyone. If you get nothing else from this book, please get this message. First, do NOT use Crisco as a tanning agent. By all means, go soak up the sun and get your natural Vitamin D from the sunshine, in moderation, but please use a good SPF when you're out in the sun—always.

Believe the professionals when they tell you to protect your skin early in life, and it will take care of you later in life. They're right. And don't forget to put SPF on your hands. I have heard that you can tell a woman's age by her hands. I don't know if that's true, but why take the chance?

Words of Wisdom: If you want to do an online assessment of your skin and look for some recommendations on skincare and cosmetic products that are over the counter, then try the Neutrogena 360®Assessment[5] on its website. (QR Code link is in Appendix B.) If you need more help than that, get into a dermatologist's office for some guidance.

Skin Cancer Awareness: Neutrogena also offers a monthly sign-up reminder for you to conduct your self-checks for potential skin issues related to sun exposure. Please consider signing up. Take care of yourself. You deserve it.

Should you be looking for that sun-kissed look but without all that UVA/UVB damage to your skin, I highly recommend you use the at-home self-tanning lotions and sprays or treat yourself to a spray tan. These products have come a long way in the past few years.

"GIRLS JUST WANT TO HAVE FUN" —Cyndi Lauper
You know it!

"SUNNY DAYS" —Lighthouse
I remember the days when lying in the sun and listening
to my favourite music station was pure bliss.

"SOAK UP THE SUN" —Sheryl Crowe
This song makes you want to tell everyone to lighten up.

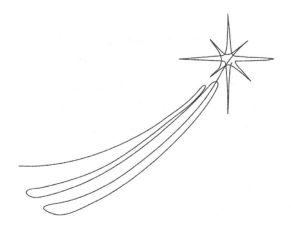

CHAPTER 10

Complexion Changes
Wrinkle Wrinkle Little Star

The wrinkles... Oh, yes, the wrinkles. This was a tough pill to swallow as a woman who has always taken care of her appearance. I got 'em—of course. I wish I didn't have to see them, deal with them, and get judged by them. They suck! This is not breaking news to you, I'm sure.

Wrinkles are an inevitable part of the aging process for men and women. They are a big deal for many women, and I include myself here. Our never-ending search for the magic elixir to eliminate our wrinkles makes cosmetic and skincare companies extremely successful.

And if you are struggling with your physical appearance, technology has significantly advanced throughout my lifetime, and I daresay it will continue to advance rapidly. This technology is also making cosmetic and surgical practitioners extremely popular and prosperous. I am grateful if they can provide or recommend effective solutions for us.

I also don't judge anyone who seeks out and tries various lotions, potions, and procedures. That is none of my business.

I have not yet found the magic elixir, nor have I found the Fountain of Youth. I shall boldly continue searching for both, but meanwhile, I will continue to practice good skin care. From my sun-worshipping teenage years, I learned that I should have protected and nurtured my skin as early in life as possible. Now I know better.

Huge disclaimer here: I am not promoting the use of any external or invasive medical or cosmetic procedures. That is not my intent. My intention is only to acknowledge the existence of an incredible abundance of cosmetics and techniques at our disposal. I have never even broken a bone, and the thought of surgery and "going under" using anesthesia frightens me. I suspect that's just the control freak in me showing up. But, all this said, for me, ain't nothin' off the table.

Should I decide to have "work done," it will be my decision. I neither want nor require unsolicited external judgment; if I want an opinion, I will ask. I'm a grown-ass woman, confident I can make decisions for myself. So should you.

Just be smart about it and go to a licensed, reputable physician or technician if you're considering this. Do your homework well. Ask for referrals. Look up their ratings and reviews online. This is not the time to make knee-jerk decisions or go to a friend-of-a-friend's place for a DIY Botox™ party. Yikes. Work with a qualified professional. Seriously. You are worth it.

Wrinkle-fighting aside, I believe our wrinkles and smile lines directly reflect how we have lived our lives—with a great deal of laughter, concentration, stress, and other environmental things, like not using sunscreen when we should have.

Embrace those laugh lines; keep laughing and enjoying yourself. You are beautiful, just as you are.

Words of Wisdom: Please practice good and consistent skincare and make it a daily ritual. Use moisturizer and SPF products daily. An abundance of information about skin analysis, product recommendations, and how-to-apply videos is available. Educate yourself and make your skincare a priority in your day.

I promise a high ROI (return on investment)—for you! if you lovingly care for your skin throughout your life. Your future self will thank you.

Words of Wisdom: Additionally, consider buying yourself some silk pillowcases if you want to treat yourself to a bit of indulgence while you sleep. You will love the impact they have on your skin and hair. Plus, they feel so luxurious. And for those who might be experiencing the odd "night sweat," try them. They feel so welcomingly cool.

"WHEN I'M 64" —The Beatles
As time goes by, we'll both be getting older.
And then, *Pooof!* We're 64!

"YOU WEAR IT WELL" —Rod Stewart
Look at you! I agree with Mr. Stewart.
You do wear it well. You are so fine.

CHAPTER 11

Tech Neck Changes

Heads-up!

*"Each man's destiny is hung like a
medallion around his neck."*

—CHARLES LE GAI EATON

aton's quote above refers to our fate and the inevitability of
our destined paths in life. At the risk of offending anyone
who might be devoted to Eaton's work, I daresay this quote now
takes on a new tone and visual interpretation of the impact technology will have on all of us in the future.

Because we are all married to our cell phones and other devices, our heads are bowed a great deal of the day. We all have seen people reading their cell phones while in business meetings, on the subway, in restaurants, in bars, in social settings (where we used to speak face-to-face, remember those days?), and even while walking across the street. And, despite the well-known risks, we still see people texting on their cell phones while driving, which is a whole different rant—don't even get me started.

I recently went on a date with a gentleman, and when we got to the restaurant, after ordering our drinks, he pulled out his phone and started checking his Facebook™ account. I must not be the sparkling and witty conversationalist I believed myself to be if I couldn't beat his buddy's fishing pictures, or whatever he was looking at. Could that not have waited? If he wanted to "catch" this woman, he'd have to ignore a good photo of a freshly caught walleye.

But come on. We can't even lift our heads, get out of bed, or enjoy a few minutes of real-life conversation without checking our phones? Our phones are addictive and indispensable; somehow, we have allowed them to take over our power.

So, what does this mean insofar as our health and appearance are concerned? We will have to deal with our necks showing signs of accelerated aging. It's called "Tech Neck" (aka "Text Neck"), and I bet you see the effects already. Look in the mirror and take a slow, appraising look at your neck... What do you see? Incidentally, wouldn't a neck and shoulder massage feel good too?

*"Tech neck, the act of stressing muscles while
using phones, tablets, and computers, resulting
in neck and shoulder pain, stiffness, and
soreness, is a problem that is getting worse.*

*"When you're working on a computer or looking down
at your phone, the muscles in the back of the neck have
to contract to hold your head up. These muscles can get
overly tired and sore... That's what we call 'tech neck.'*

*"At [holding our head] just 45 degrees,
your neck muscles are doing the work of
lifting a 50-pound bag of potatoes."* [6]
—DR. K. DANIEL RIEW

Indeed, the more concerning problem of Tech Neck is the impact on our neck and shoulder muscles. Be aware of this: 50 pounds of potatoes! I'm not sure I could carry that in my arms, let alone around my neck. Yowza!

In addition, our cell phone and personal device usage also keep our necks and throats in a consistent crimp. I suspect the long-term effects on our skin will not go undetected.

I predict Tech Neck will become a raging epidemic if it isn't already. So maybe we will start to take pride in our crimpled Tech Necks because they will be a universal norm, or even a part of our destiny, just like the "medallion" in Eaton's quote above.

Alternatively, we may fight Tech Neck to the death by investing in all types of lotions, potions, and procedures. I suspect this will rise to the top of the plastic surgeons' and cosmetic practitioners' repertoires shortly. I also anticipate our chiropractors and massage therapists will be building up a smorgasbord of Tech Neck treatments for us to consider.

I'm prepared to do whatever it takes to tame Tech Neck, but don't even think about taking away my cell phone. I am consciously trying to remember to hold my cell phone and tablet at eye level whenever possible—ditto my PC screen. I choose not to work with my laptop resting on my lap but with the screen at eye level. I'm not sure if any of these actions I am taking will have a measurable positive impact, but I have convinced myself that they can't hurt.

Words of Wisdom: Be conscious of the impact your electronic devices will have on your neck and shoulder muscles. Be sure to take breaks from your tech and stretch and massage those areas. And be sure to take loving care of the skin on your neck just as much as you do the skin on your face.

Words of Wisdom: And if you are one of those people who believe that you have mastered the ability to text and drive, you haven't. Seriously. Stop that sh*t immediately. You have not been blessed with this ability because no one has. Please stop checking your phone while behind the wheel of a motor vehicle or while riding a bike. You might also think about not checking your phone as you cross streets.

If the safety of yourself and others hasn't already stopped you from these practices, consider giving your neck and throat a well-deserved break from tech while driving and walking as a preventative step against Tech Neck.

Words of Wisdom: If you are out on a date, in a business meeting, or engaged in any form of live discussion with another human being, consider putting your phone on silent, turning it over, turning it off, or better yet, why not tuck it away until you have finished your conversation?

The most respectful thing you can do is participate in a real conversation entirely without technology detracting and distracting you. Wouldn't it be nice, as a common practice, for people to establish a mutual agreement at the start of a meeting, *"Hey, would you mind if we put our phones away? So we can focus our attention here, now, on each other."* Imagine!

Maybe I'm considered "old school" with this approach, but I think good manners should never go out of style.

"**TELEPHONE LINE**" —Electric Light Orchestra
Here's a song that takes this Boomer back to the '70s, long before cell phones, when we actually spoke on the telephone.
"Doo-wop, doo-be-doo-doo-wop, doo-wah, doo-lang"

CHAPTER 12

Vision Changes

"I Can See Clearly Now"

—JOHNNY NASH

I started wearing glasses in Grade 6 and persevered through all the "Four Eyes" taunts—(is that still a thing?) and continued through until I was eighteen when I was working and could buy my first pair of contact lenses. I wore contact lenses until I was in my early 40s.

At that time, I started to notice that even with my contacts, I was having some issues reading books, and I found that I had to keep pushing back my chair to be able to read what was on my computer screen. Although it creeps up on you, it just seems to hit you one day, and it was literally like, *"Holy Sh*t. It has happened to me."* All those jokes people made about needing longer arms weren't a joke. But I wasn't ready for longer arms, nor did I want to revert to wearing glasses all the time.

For me, vision changes rate a little lower on the "Aging Sucks" scale than some of the other changes, perhaps because I always had some sort of vision issues since Grade 6, and I have learned to take them in stride.

Has this happened to you yet? If not, brace yourself because it likely will. You may want to start thinking about a solution. Longer arms? No. New glasses? Reader glasses? Magnifying glass? Binoculars? They even have multifocal contact lenses now.

According to the website *Presbyopia Life*:

"Many people begin to notice changes in their near vision around 40. The ability to focus on things such as phones, tablets, newspapers, and up-close objects steadily declines until around 60. The culprit behind age-related near vision loss is called presbyopia.

"Presbyopia is part of the natural aging process. This progressive condition is characterized by changes in your eye's lens. The lens is responsible for refracting light toward the retina at the back of the eye. Presbyopia causes the lens to stiffen and change shape and/or size, making it more difficult to see clearly at a close distance."[7]

My optometrist suggested that I consider laser surgery to correct my distance vision. I was forewarned that laser eye surgery would be a fantastic solution to correct my distance vision, eliminating the need for glasses and contact lenses. Still, it would be at the expense of my up-close vision. I was told I would eventually need reading glasses to bolster my up-close vision. That seemed like a small price to pay. So, off I went to have laser eye surgery. What fantastic freedom that gave me! I saw the world through what seemed like a brand-new pair of eyes.

I had my laser surgery at a clinic two hours away from home. I drove home the day after my surgery, and I remember stopping along the highway to test my new eyes. I marvelled that I could now see the definition in the trees' leaves, where before all I could see was just a great mass of greenery. Louis Armstrong was right— "What a Wonderful World." I felt like I saw the whole world for the first time.

And, of course, my optometrist was correct. I eventually became reliant on reading glasses. Since then, I have bought myself dozens of pairs. I have them sprinkled throughout my home, vehicle, and purses because yet another "sucky" thing about getting older is that you forget where you left them. So I now have all the bases covered.

Some 20+ years later, my laser eye surgery still provides me with near perfect distance vision. Although I suspect my visual acuity will decline as I get older—another one of those inverse relationships. I have friends who have had cataract surgery. During the last few years of her life, my mother was fighting macular degeneration.

If I am following the typical aging trajectory, I suspect the next change in my vision will be cataracts. I understand that nearly 60% of all people over 80 will need to deal with cataracts.

Dr. Denny Birring, Optometrist, IRIS Clinic, indicates, "*Overexposure to UV rays can be a factor in our vision loss as we age.*" Dr. Birring also reports that, "*80% of the UV damage we experience that will contribute to our declining eyesight will occur from birth through to age 20.*"[8]

When I think about the sun exposure of my youth, I shouldn't be surprised by the corresponding decline in my vision over the years.

Additionally, our eyes are now subject to extensive blue light exposure from our devices. Consider investing in a pair of blue light lenses to wear while working on your computer for extended periods.

Okay, here's something I want to ask you if you're 50+ years of age: Have you started to notice that you turn down the car radio when you want to see better?

It's crazy; one minute, I was young, fun, and singing out loud to the music in my car, and the next minute, I was turning down the car radio so I could see better! I still do.

Although vision changes are a common side effect of the aging process for many of us, I believe that as I have gone through the years and picked up all kinds of wisdom, one of the greatest Superpowers I've found is this...

> *"Even though my eyesight has weakened, I can see through people's bullsh*t so much better."*

I have seen and heard so much garbage that people shovel out. I think to myself, *"Really? Like... really?"* With or without my reading glasses and laser-enhanced vision, I can spot a bullsh*tter from miles away. If you're over 40, or even 30, I bet you can, too. Am I right? If so, you've got a Superpower you need to keep fully dialed to the max at all times: Your Bullsh*t Detector.

Words of Wisdom: Don't be swayed by a bullsh*tter; they can be as smooth as silk. If something doesn't sound right, challenge it. Trust your instincts. Don't be a weak one in the herd, or they will make you their prey. Your instincts are part of your Superpowers;

use them. See, hear, and even feel with your intuition. (I talk about Intuition more in Chapter 35.) Even Willie Nelson sings about this in his beautiful "Dusty Bottles" song.

Words of Wisdom: Invest in good sunglasses for your eyes (at any age, but the earlier, the better). Ensure the sunglasses have good UV protection. "When buying a new pair of sunglasses, always choose those labelled: "100% UV protection" or "UV 400." [9] If you're unsure about the level of protection of your current sunglasses (or your children's), your local optometrist or eyewear store should be able to check them for you.

Words of Wisdom: If you're wondering if you're at the stage where reader glasses might be useful, consider taking an online eye test from readers.com. (See link in Appendix B.) Please remember that any online test is not a viable substitution for a complete eye exam by a licensed optometrist.

> *"People will show you their true colours—*
> *just make sure you're not colourblind."*

"I CAN SEE CLEARLY NOW" —Johnny Nash
This one is from the 1972 archives.

"WHAT A WONDERFUL WORLD" —Louis Armstrong
Who doesn't love this song?

"DUSTY BOTTLES" —Willie Nelson
Queue up this beautiful song. Willie encourages
you to share a beer with Father Time to reflect
on your life and embrace your age.

CHAPTER 13

Hearing Changes

Listen up!

*Y*es, there can be yet another decline we could encounter as we grow older. This time, it's one of our other senses: our hearing.

To be clear, I am not speaking about hearing loss resulting from any accident or injury. I am only addressing hearing loss that comes from the passage of time.

The National Institute on Aging indicates:

"Age-related hearing loss (presbycusis) is the loss of hearing that gradually occurs in most of us as we grow older. It is one of the most common conditions affecting older and elderly adults.

"Approximately one in three people in the United States between the ages of 65 and 74 has hearing loss, and nearly half of those older than 75 have difficulty hearing. Hearing loss can also make it hard to enjoy talking with family and friends, leading to feelings of isolation." Canadian data is similar.

"Age-related hearing loss most often occurs in both ears, affecting them equally. Because the loss is gradual, you may not realize that you've lost some of your ability to hear.

"There are many causes of age-related hearing loss. Most commonly, it arises from changes in the inner ear as we age, but it can also result from changes in the middle ear or complex changes along the nerve pathways from the ear to the brain. Certain medical conditions and medications may also play a role." [10]

Because hearing loss can sneak up on us, many of us may not even realize we have it. It is very common.

Words of Wisdom: It might be helpful to take a quick five-minute online test from "Hearing Life Canada" to see how you're doing. (See Link in Appendix B.) As I'm sure you know, an online test should never replace an actual auditory test conducted by a professional.

"**LISTEN TO THE MUSIC**" —Doobie Brothers
Just turn up the volume and let this music transport you.
Whoa-oh!

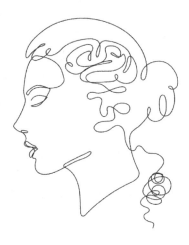

CHAPTER 14

Cognitive & Mental Changes

Oh, where was I?

*H*ave I forgotten a few things from time to time? Yes, of course, and I bet most people have, no matter their age. That said, I can't help but notice that it's happening more often. Brain fog is one of those annoying symptoms that comes along with menopause for many women.

I am not at the point where I am overly concerned, but I'm at the *"What did I come in here for?"* stage sometimes. Then it comes back to me. Probably my glasses, even though they're sprinkled all over my house. Hmmm, perhaps I should be more concerned?

Now that I am retired and don't have the intensity and structure of a corporate workday to keep me cognitively engaged and "on" all day, it's easy to fall into a more relaxed mental state. This is good. It's one of the beautiful outcomes of retirement. I think I have finally learned what work/life balance really means. I don't know if that equates to "too little, too late," but I am privileged now to have the luxury of living in that balanced state—as I define it, not as an employer might define it.

I had just retired when the Pandemic hit, so I wondered and worried about how my former colleagues and friends managed their enforced work-from-home lifestyle by balancing childcare and schooling in their children's enforced school-from-home format. I cannot imagine how they managed to maintain healthy and stable work/life balance throughout. They must have been frigging exhausted.

In my retirement, I purposefully challenge myself to keep mentally sharp. I have found that even something as simple and carefree as doing online crossword puzzles and paintings are fantastic fun ways to stay attentive and to keep the neurons snapping. I still love to read and can completely lose myself in great stories that transport me to other times and places.

I can understand how easy it would be to float softly into the ethers and not push myself to keep mentally strong and relevant or up to date with the world around me. I don't want to become mentally complacent. I suspect that would be a slippery downward slope.

I know that I have not yet suffered any worrisome signs that might signal the onset of cognitive decline. I also know that the future could hold some disappointments and challenges in this arena.

In researching this book, I found a fantastic organization called the Food for the Brain Foundation. Their mission is:

"To raise awareness of the importance of optimum nutrition in mental health. We are a not-for-profit charity working to inform organizations and empower individuals to change their diet and lifestyle and take greater control of their own mental health." [11]

Their website is very well done, and their scientifically backed research is laid out in easy-to-understand terms, presenting optimized food choices for people of all ages as we go through our Life's Trimesters. I highly recommend that you check out their website and apply this information in the ways that work for you.

Words of Wisdom: The Food for the Brain Foundation has a free online "Cognitive Functioning Test" that allows you to take a 20-minute test and will measure your cognitive functioning. Additionally, if you register, you automatically will be sent a test annually to keep ongoing measures of your cognitive abilities. (See link in Appendix B.) Brilliant! Please do yourself a favour and take this test. It is free.

Words of Wisdom: I also have found some fun apps you can sign up for (free of charge) that provide great puzzles and games that will entertain you (and seamlessly) and keep your mind active and engaged. (Refer to Appendix B.)

Words of Wisdom: I invite you to find activities and play games that stimulate your mind, no matter your age, but particularly once you are in the 3rd Trimester (60+) of your life. Bonus: You will get an even bigger mental boost if you play games that challenge you to race against the clock.

Don't let your mind get rusty. The thing about rust is that it's insidious—it can very quickly take over if you let it. Keep levelling up. This is a "must do," not a "nice to do." Please get going.

"LEVEL UP" —Ciara
It's time to take things up a notch. Level up!

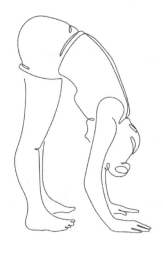

CHAPTER 15

Physical Mobility Changes

Houston, we have a problem!

I am sitting in my makeshift office (aka my dining table) at almost 5 p.m. Even though every day in retirement is pretty fantastic, I have had one of those "fan-frickin'-tastic" days.

Alexa woke me up and gave me good news about today's weather forecast. I had a great night's sleep, bounced out of bed and was in that "make-my-bed-right-away" mood. So, with a freshly made bed, feeling good and already ahead of my usual routine, I found myself dancing out to the kitchen, following the scent of freshly brewed coffee (I set my timer last night). My first cup of coffee tasted heavenly (you know how your first cup of coffee tastes better on some days than others?), and after breakfast, I was energized and ready to *carpe diem*.

Oh yeah, baby! I was in that invincible *"Bring. It. On."* kind of mood. You know what I'm talking about, don't you? Yeah, you do. In the spirit of keeping pace with my high-energy *"unstoppable"* vibe, I jumped on my bike, went to the pickleball courts, played a couple of games, then biked to the gym, did some strength training, and then biked home.

I spent the rest of the day running errands, tidying up, you know… the usual retiree stuff.

Sounds impressive, doesn't it? Until you find out how I am feeling. Well, I am mentally happy that I did all these things and feel quite proud of myself; however, physically, I will be hurting tomorrow morning. But, as John Mellencamp sings, it "Hurts So Good." Yes, I know his song isn't about exercise, well, at least not exercise in the pickleball kind of way. *Hehe.* But you knew what I meant, didn't you?

You have likely overdone it by pushing yourself beyond your physical boundaries at one time or another. And it "hurt so good" because it was rewarding and invigorating, and all those good endorphins were pumping through your body, masking the physical aches and pains you would feel later. No pain, no gain… *Yeah, right.*

The good news is that I can still enjoy physical activity and exercise, and I am incredibly fortunate and grateful for that. But will I be groaning when I try to stand up again? (I have been sitting here for just shy of an hour.)—I suspect so. I remember the days when I would not have groaned standing up after even more challenging workouts and being seated for extended periods. Am I out of shape? Not entirely, but I don't believe I would be mistaken for Jillian Michaels, either. Clearly, *I'm Not 20 Anymore.*

As an over-the-top grandmother, I love to get down on the floor and play with my grandbabies. They motivate me to keep myself in good physical shape. While I can no longer do the splits I did as a high-school cheerleader, I am happy that I can still get up quickly enough after being on the floor with them. Now, I am content to be able to coach my grandchildren as they try to do the splits.

I am mobile and extremely grateful every day that I can do whatever I want at this stage. I am fit, vital, and healthy, and I hope that my outer being reflects the radiance I feel inside. I understand that someday I will not have the luxury or privilege to do what I can now. We all know friends and family who are not as fortunate with their mobility and have not been able to escape the physical pain that sometimes comes along for the ride on our life journeys. My heart honestly does go out to those people, and I would never want to minimize their struggles; someday, I suspect I will have my own.

Advice for staying physically fit and mobile was readily available to me through the years. When I was younger, I could bounce back relatively quickly from any breaks in my exercise activities.

As a result, I lapsed into thinking that I could always do this, so I didn't pay much attention to it. I have learned that my body is not as resilient as it once was.

Physically, getting older is not for sissies, and it sucks. However, I believe I have had enough challenging life experiences to make me strong enough to take it on. So, I choose to go forward and do what I can when I can.

Additionally, I am aware that technology has advanced significantly to support people with physical issues, giving them another chance they wouldn't have had fifty years ago.

"Hip and joint replacements are reportedly the 2nd and 3rd highest types of surgeries [after Caesareans] in Canada and the U.S." [12]

Isn't that an incredible statistic? I know several people who have had hip or joint replacements, and they say they are life-changing and gave them back their mobility without pain. I wonder what the technology will be like when my children and grandchildren are my age.

Words of Wisdom: Stay as mobile as possible, starting as early as you can in your life. Today is better than someday. Admittedly, I let myself lax into a more sedentary state in my late 50s, and I am paying the price for that now. I have no excuse for that, and I own it. I have set myself up to work much harder to return to my version of my best physical state.

It's a long climb back, and gravity is not my friend. That's another 1-2 punch I'm up against, and it will be the same for you. My strongest advice would be to get ahead of it and stay ahead of it as soon as you can.

Just keep physically moving for as long as you can, as often as your body will tolerate without damage. I'm serious. Besides sunscreen, exercise is the closest we have to a Fountain of Youth. Don't stop.

Through the Pandemic, I also built myself an Alexa playlist for my newly formatted at-home exercise activities; I suspect you may already have your own. I am more likely to get mobile and physical when I play some of my favourite music; believe me, there are days when I need to be enticed. Some days, I just don't wanna be bothered, so I need Geri Halliwell to belt out: "It's Raining Men" to get me moving. "*Hallelujah!*"

I play little head games with myself while working out and listening to music; for example, I push myself to do a few more reps until the song ends, but I think everybody does this. And, if I'm not pumping iron to the tune (which is highly fricking likely), you will find me dancing and singing along, taking the lead on vocals. Sometimes I am on air guitar, and sometimes on the keyboard. I live alone... Can you tell?

If I am out for a walk, I also use this time to do some levelling up. I love to listen to podcasts while I'm walking. Some great podcasts are available; go surf through them and find your soul tribe and what is meaningful to you.

I have listened to Arlene Dickinson's "*Reinvention*" podcast [13] and was mesmerized by her illustrious guests and how they got their start in life and which detours came along for them that changed the trajectory of their lives. (See Part V, Chapter 32.) And who doesn't like a good strong dose of Oprah Winfrey? Her podcasts and guests are phenomenal.

In my way of thinking, I am doing two good things for myself:

staying active by walking and levelling up by listening to people much smarter than me. Win-Win. I usually download a few podcasts before my walks to motivate me to walk longer. I'm not particularly eager to leave any podcasts mid-stream.

Do you have any favourite podcasts that you would like to share? I am open to hearing your ideas as I find the vast array of podcasts overwhelming. Overall, though, how lucky are we to have access to wisdom like this?

"HURTS SO GOOD" —John Mellencamp
Rock out to this one. This song is meant to be cranked up!

"IT'S RAINING MEN" —Geri Halliwell
Geri tells us the street's the place to go… just about
half-past ten. Can I get another "Hallelujah?"

CHAPTER 16

Menopause: The BIG Change

I Finally Got a Smokin' Hot Body!

How could any woman who writes a book about how Aging Sucks not mention menopause? I have three words to capture the essence of menopause (and yes, I know these aren't words in the true sense, but they capture it beautifully):

OMG!

I am officially in post-menopause. Woo-hoo! From my experiential point of view, going through menopause was one bewildering ride from pre (or peri)-menopause through to my current menopausal state. Brace yourself—you too, gentlemen.

By the way, gentlemen, do yourselves a big favour and study these symptoms below. Commit them to memory. Recite them daily if necessary. Be prepared. And can I ask you to please be supportive?

This journey also tends to sneak up on you. I will not sugar-coat it; it's a hormonal roller coaster ride from hell! At least, that is my opinion. I know some women have been fortunate enough to sail through menopause without experiencing any or many symptoms, and I am envious of them.

The National Institute of Aging (NIA) says, *"Menopause is caused by the cessation in production of estrogen and progesterone in the ovaries, which results in the end of menstruation."*

There are several stages to menopause: pre-menopause aka peri-menopause, menopause, and post-menopause. Honestly, I found it hard to discern a distinct difference between my regular cycles and the pre-menopause onset.

At first, you might notice a few changes to your monthly cycles, where they start to become bi-or-tri-monthly, a little longer, or maybe a little shorter. Oddly, even the pre-menstrual syndrome (PMS) symptoms don't follow the same predictable monthly pattern as they had for the past 40 years. *(That's right, you will have a monthly menstrual cycle for ~40 years!)*

No, the emotional *bit-o-bitch* moments in peri-menopause that I experienced seemed to come along much more frequently and at times, a little more intensely than any monthly PMS symptoms I had previously "bestowed" upon others. So here's the kicker: I was not yet self-aware, but everyone else around me had noticed "The Bitch is Back" (Elton John).

The next telltale sign is that you'll take your jacket off when everyone else needs to keep theirs on. Ditto for the gloves, hats, and scarves. All good. No big deal, right? You will feel like you have this little fluctuating temperature thing under control. But, you will also notice how strange it is that your "head" gets so hot. *I know!—weird, right?*

And along the way, you finally become fully aware of both the acceleration and intensity in your *bit-o-bitch* ("BOB") moments. Thankfully, someone has been brave (or scared) enough to tell you, likely your partner or your children. Your co-workers have probably learned to keep their distance.

So, now that you're aware your BOB moments have taken on a life of their own, you decide to "boss up" and regain control of your emotions.

So here's some good news, you are much wiser by this time in your life, and you will know intuitively when you need to temper those hormonally charged *"F*ck you!"* moments or when you need to let BOB and your hormones do the talking for you. It's liberating.

So, at this stage, you have convinced yourself that the pre-menopause symptoms are manageable, and you do what you need to do, and you're likely not paying too much attention to them. And so your very hectic life goes on.

Then one fine day, without any warning whatsoever, you will think you're having a heart attack or a stroke or something equally debilitating, but it's sooooo much more humiliating.

I distinctly remember the first time I had a hot flash. It's true. You never forget your first; that goes for hot flashes too.

I legitimately thought I was having a heart attack; it stopped me in my tracks, and I just sat there absolutely bewildered, scared, and trying to remember to breathe to see if it would help bring down my sky-rocketing body temperature. My heart was beating wildly. I broke out into an immediate sweat, and then I was left cold, clammy, and shivering for the finale. I suspect it was over in a few minutes, but it felt like an hour. I remember that each of those sensations was as intense as the next.

It shook me up, physically and emotionally. It took me a while to understand and accept that I had started the journey through menopause. The hot flash seemed to make it official. I was in my mid-40s.

Life was a blur between work, family, kids' sporting events, and business travel, so I wasn't paying that much attention to my monthly cycles. I had already had my children, and birth control wasn't an issue.

Strangely enough, despite countless conversations with my mom, I never had a meaningful conversation with her about menopause.

As a young girl, I remember overhearing my mother and aunt talking about other women going through "the change." I had no idea what that meant, but these conversations were always spoken in low voices with a tone of secrecy (presumably so the menfolk wouldn't hear?) When I would ask what it meant, I was told, *"Never mind—you don't need to know,"* and as a young girl, I didn't need to know. Yet. Additionally, going through "the change" was never discussed in school, so it wasn't even on my radar.

I haven't heard menopause called "the change" for a long time— that's good. Have you? As a young girl, I recall those words conjured up some wild theories on what that could mean.

I remember one morning; when I was in my mid-20s, my mother walking down the hall towards the kitchen where I was having a coffee. Actually, she was stomping and wildly flapping her arms, and the entire time, she was talking quite loudly about how hot it was in the house. And she wasn't very happy.

With all that stomping and flapping, she was almost airborne when she made it to the kitchen, asking, *"How can it be so hot in here so early in the morning?"* When I told her it wasn't, I asked, *"Mom, do you think you're having a hot flash?"* She became quite indignant, stopped her flapping, glared and me, and declared, *"No goddammed way am I having a hot flash!"*

I remember being taken aback. I hurried off to the coffee pot to break the stink-eye stare I was being given and said something like, *"Okey-dokey, Mom, how about another cup of coffee then?"* The subject was closed. I don't remember re-opening the topic with her ever again. I wish I had.

I have personally been through the same "stomp and flap" routine on many occasions, and believe me, I have even demonstrated a

"BOB" attitude more than a few times. So, I have learned that I will never ask a middle-aged woman amid her "stomp and flap" routine if she is having a hot flash. I now know to hand her a tissue (or even better, a roll of paper towels, or cool washcloth), and I will get her a cold drink because she is in no mood for chit-chat. Take heed y'all.

Yes, I can confirm, through my firsthand knowledge, that there can be some heightened emotions that come along with "the change." It's akin to PMS, but there didn't seem to be a defined rhythm or pattern, as there was with PMS.

And if you have not yet entered pre-menopause or menopause, let me offer you an excerpt from the U.S. National Institute of Aging (NIA), which outlines the highlights of this time in a woman's life:

- "The menopausal transition most often begins between ages 45 and 55. It usually lasts about 7 years but can last as long as 14 years."

    7-14 years? Are you f*cking kidding me?

- "During the menopausal transition, the body's production of estrogen and progesterone, two hormones produced by the ovaries, varies greatly.
- "Bones become less dense, making women more vulnerable to fractures.
- "During this period, the body begins to use energy differently, fat cells change, and women may gain weight more easily."

YUP. This happens. Also, continuing in the spirit of my over-sharing, the larger breasts I always wanted in my younger years showed up during this time. I also have gone up a full-dress size since I entered menopause, probably to balance out my larger breasts. Give me a break already!

Weight gain through menopause is challenging as you get into your 60s. I have learned that losing weight at any time is difficult, but when you're in menopause, I am not going to lie; it is really fricking difficult. So here's another heads-up: the extra weight also seems to be headed right to our mid-sections. WTF!

The NIA defines a hot flash as:

- "A sudden feeling of heat in the upper part or all of your body.
- "Your face and neck become flushed.
- "Red blotches might appear on your chest, back and arms.
- "Heavy sweating and cold shivering can follow.
- "Most hot flashes last between 30 seconds and 10 minutes. They can happen several times in an hour, a few times a day, or once or twice a week.
- "Women can experience hot flash episodes for several years during and after menopause." [14]

Isn't that a fricking bright and cheery list of symptoms to consider? That is a perfectly accurate description of my first hot flash, but the heat was extreme, and my heart was racing, so you can understand why I thought it was a heart attack.

Let me share with you one of my many "tropical moment" stories that got me into my doctor's office as soon as I got home from a business trip. The NIA would describe this as *"a clash between my work responsibilities and a hot flash."* I, however, describe it as one of the most embarrassing times in my professional life.

I had to make a critical sales pitch to a gentleman (age ~45, I was 54), a senior executive of an account I managed. There was a great deal riding on this program for my company and theirs. Despite several attempts by others from my company, no one had been able to "seal the deal" on this initiative.

I was confident that I could. I knew all the buttons and levers to push and pull that would benefit our respective companies. We were having a roundtable meeting in his office; no PowerPoint presentation was involved that would serve as a visual distraction.

I took the lead at the meeting and got into the pitch, sharing all the initiative's key strategies, tactics, and projected financials. The meeting was going exceptionally well, and we were in meaningful dialogue about the program. The customer was fully engaged and excited about the plan I was outlining, and we were already talking about the next steps.

We were about forty minutes into our meeting when suddenly, without warning, a massive inferno was lit from within me (like *WHOOOOOF!*), an intense heat quickly engulfed my body.

For me, it was always hard to identify the genesis location of a hot flash; it always seemed to start somewhere deep inside the core. And there has never been any pre-trigger or physical warning that a hot flash is coming. It is always a surprise.

I was wearing the usual business attire, a jacket, pants, and a blouse. Off came my jacket as quickly as I could without clawing and ripping it off and scaring the sh*t out of him.

I could feel a nice trickle of perspiration wriggling its way down my chest and into my cleavage. I was grateful that my dark-coloured blouse absorbed it all without being very noticeable.

And I could feel my hair getting wet at the nape of my neck, while trying to pretend nothing was going on, or wrong, with my flushed and perspiring face. *Like, that's normal?!*

The meeting continued, and I really needed to reach down into my briefcase to get a tissue to mop off my forehead and neckline. I did it all as gracefully as possible while continuing the discussion. I didn't miss a beat. By the way, I "dabbed"—I didn't "mop," honestly. But I wanted to "mop," get naked, and run into an ice-cold shower.

The gentleman I was having a meeting with didn't flinch at all. We just continued with our discussion, and if he knew what was going on, he didn't let on, and for that, I am incredibly grateful.

And in case you're wondering, I "sealed the deal" on this initiative with the customer. Oh hell yeah! I was on fire, literally and figuratively. Like Alicia Keyes's song: I was a "Girl on Fire."

While this wasn't the first time I had suffered through a hot flash, it was undoubtedly the most embarrassing, and I couldn't afford to have to deal with that again in a professional setting. As soon as I got back into my car after that meeting, I was on the phone with my doctor booking an appointment to arrange a consultation about Hormone Replacement Therapy (HRT).

I was cleared for HRT by my doctor, and for me, it was an absolute life-changer. Again, I am not a physician, and I am not in a qualified position to advise you on this. That level of expertise is far outside my wheelhouse. I am only sharing my personal circumstances with you. HRT controlled my internal furnace and kept it at a more stable and predictable level.

I know that other women have had success managing menopausal symptoms without HRT, and you should always do your homework and discuss this with your doctor before taking anyone's advice. You know your body best.

Now, in my 60s, I am in post-menopause, and because I could only stay on HRT for five years (doctor's orders), I am very happy that I'm doing great. I still have the odd hot flash, but they are a thing of the past for the most part. Every once in a while, I will still have one just as a reminder not to get too comfortable.

I know women who have been enduring menopausal symptoms for more than twenty years. I also know women who have not been fazed in any way by the transition into menopause and have never experienced a hot flash. So for those fortunate ones, if you want some idea of what a hot flash feels like, listen to Nelly's song, "It's Hot in Here."

It is not lost on me that Nelly's song is obviously about a sexual encounter, not menopause. But interestingly enough, some of the lyrics aptly describe the beginnings of a hot flash for a woman. The difference is that you want to rip your clothes off and throw yourself into a freezer, not into bed with your lover. The struggle is real.

And if you are thinking, *"Well, okay, I can handle a few hot flashes,"* then kudos to you, my cool little cucumber. Let's hope that you can also get through a full-blown night sweat. These are, in a word, "brutal." Many women going through menopause will endure night sweats. But, as with hot flashes, there is no forewarning.

Imagine this: You are in a deep sleep, and something slowly starts to come to your awareness. You're a little groggy, and of course, try to go back to sleep. But your hormones have something else in mind while you're in bed *(and no, your hormones are not directing you to the "good stuff," if you know what I mean)*. That is the farthest thing from your mind.

And as you try to go back to sleep, you push and kick your bedsheets off because you just realized that you're feeling a little too warm, and then you try to drift back off to sleep.

Right about now, your hormones manifest their power over you with a full-body heat explosion, which results in your entire body being immediately and thoroughly drenched in sweat. This is not a light, delicate sheen. Nope. It's like you just stepped out of a sauna. Your hair is even wet!

And now you are fully awake and ripping off your nightclothes. You also realize your bedsheets are soaking wet. But it's not over yet. Because now, as all that moisture starts to evaporate and your entire body swings from an inferno to an icy-cold state... the shivering starts. There is no way you can go back to bed and sleep on those wet sheets.

You start stripping the bed; your partner, if you have one, is undoubtedly well aware of what's happening. Hopefully, you'll get some assistance in the 2:15 a.m. bed remake. *[PSA to all partners of menopausal women: Help her out.]* Or, sometimes, you just grab a few dry towels and throw them over the bedsheets because all you want to do is get back to sleep quickly. A night sweat is physically exhausting.

You may encounter other symptoms as well that you might not even associate with menopause, things like migraines, anxiety or depression, memory issues, or more.

I'm telling you, this menopause stuff ain't playin'!

Are you ready for some good news about menopause? When you enter your menopausal years, you will be at the age where your life experiences have fortified your strength, wisdom, and intuition. (There's another piece of good news, which you will read about in the next chapter, but it's steamy in a different way…)

It also seemed that when I started my menopausal journey, I passed through *"The Rhett Butler Portal,"* aka the *"Frankly, I Don't Give a Damn!"* portal. Seriously. I started caring less about what others thought of me and more about what I thought of myself, which is one of the beautiful and positive outcomes of menopause. Trust me; this is an empowering portal to cross through!

Words of Wisdom: I know you will have "your first time" as well, so be mentally prepared for what to expect when a hot flash comes calling. I wasn't. It sneaked up on me, but it shouldn't have. I only paid full attention to menopause when it was happening to me.

Please take some time to make yourself aware of the symptoms *before* it happens to you. Talk to other women about it; this should not be a prohibited topic, but it still seems to be that way.

The Menopause Foundation of Canada published a Press Release on October 6, 2022, that reads, *"Landmark new research of Canadian women going through the universal experience of perimenopause/menopause reveals the real-life impact and inequities women face in a stage of life long shrouded by secrecy."*

Words of Wisdom: We can make many lifestyle changes through menopause to temper the resulting body changes. Consider options to minimize the symptoms unless you want to go hard-core and soldier on through without intervention.

You will need to do some homework on this and find an approach (i.e., diet, exercise, HRT, naturopathic remedies) that fits your lifestyle and beliefs. It is not a one-size-fits-all approach. I want to offer you a quick fix, but I have not yet discovered one.

Work with your physician or professional practitioner for guidance.

There are many books, blogs, and online resources today. I recommend the "Menopause Foundation of Canada," as a good starting point. (See link in QR Code in Appendix B.) They even have a "Menopause Symptoms Tracker." Love this!

Two other fantastic organizations are the "National Menopause Foundation" and "The North American Menopause Society." (QR Codes in Appendix B.)

Take the time to educate yourself on the symptoms and consider all the treatment options *before* it happens. It will be worth it. You are worth it.

"We need to change how we talk about 'the change.'"

"THE BITCH IS BACK" —Elton John
This one has spoken to me (and unfortunately others),
during some of my scorching and steamy times.

"HOT IN HERE" —Nelly
This is a hot and sexy song. (*Ow! Ow!*) But as I mentioned,
I had some ulterior motives for choosing this song.

"GIRL ON FIRE" —Alicia Keys

I love the energy and the power of this song for women. Ms. Keys is not singing about menopause, but in their pure sense, her "Girl on Fire" lyrics hit home for any woman who has ever melted her way through a hot flash.

CHAPTER 17

Sex and the Senior Girl

*H*ow fortunate that the topic of 'sex' follows the chapter about a 'hot body.'

It's almost laughable that I would write about this at all. Recall from my "Introduction" to the book that I am a DSWF: "Divorced Single White Female." I am not even in a committed relationship right now, so I'm not sure I got the creds to be doling out too much advice here. But I still have an excellent long-term memory.

In any case, first things first... I understand that, as the NIA reports: "*Many women also experience a decline in sexual interest and activity during their menopausal years, and they also experience some physical discomfort. This, too, can be another unfortunate symptom of a woman's journey through menopause.*"

Yup, the hits just keep on coming, don't they?

So, my advice to anyone not going through menopause is to enjoy yourselves fully right now (*wink, wink*) just in case you're one of the unfortunate ones who might lose interest once you hit menopause. So, party on! And, not to be patronizing, but be safe and smart too.

And when it comes to the discomfort part, I understand there are all kinds of excellent lubrication options out there for you on your pharmacy shelves.

Here is some encouraging news for you. Like Ms. Rexha sings in "Not 20 Anymore," can women claim that as we get older, we become better lovers? OMG! Yes! Sex does get better with age. I am much more confident in myself, my body, my femininity, Divine Feminine (DF), and Divine Masculine (DM).

We no longer have to worry about getting pregnant, (read that twice, talk about freedom!), we no longer have young children in the house inhibiting or interrupting us, and we are more willing to ask for—and do—whatever we want, in bed and out.

An additional benefit of "coming of age" is that I am far past the mating game-playing stages that had been a part of my younger years. The incomparable Tina Turner sings about this in "I Don't Wanna Lose You." Please listen to it. Ms. Turner was 50 when she released this song. It's Tina Turner—she gets it!

My kids are cringing right now, but I would have done the same if my mother had written about sex when she was 64 or any age. Yikes! I can't blame them. Sorry, kids.

Other than that, I will not say much more about sex. That's one more beautiful Superpower I have picked up through aging; how to set boundaries.

"Strong women don't have attitudes. They have standards and boundaries. So don't confuse the two."

"I DON'T WANNA LOSE YOU" —Tina Turner
Ms. Turner delivers this song in her pure Divine Feminine self.

"DEAR NO ONE" —Tori Kelly
DSWF, so yeah, I'm throwing this in the mix.

"Tennessee Whiskey" —Chris Stapleton
You have to let that voice melt all over you. It makes
women feel like their estrogen levels are on steroids (if
that's even a thing?) You'll know what I mean. Alexa
already knows I'm going to ask her to repeat this one.

"Older Women" —Ronnie McDowell
Ronnie seems to think older women
make better lovers. Just sayin'!

CHAPTER 18

Gravitational Changes

I have learned that gravity is not a menopausal woman's best friend. And I'm not just talking about what we can see happening on the outside. Some of us are aware of other internal gravitational effects, particularly if we have birthed children.

Enter: pelvic floor issues in a woman's body. We get it already. No more physical signs need to be presented for us to understand that we are going through the aging process, and it is just one more physiological change that we must adapt to.

Women who have had children know what happens to our pelvic floors, and we all diligently do Kegels to return our bodies to pre-pregnancy status. (You ARE doing your Kegels, right?) Perhaps there are not enough Kegels in the world to restore our pelvic floors to their original state, but our fight continues.

Actually, gravity is not *anyone's* best friend when it relates to our physical bodies through aging. We all recognize the mostly frontal downward trend that has been occurring in our physical bodies as well. None of us are getting any "perkier" as we get older unless you're paying for that privilege, and frankly, it is none of my business if you are. You do you.

It is doubtful that you will retain your 25-year-old physique throughout your life, and honestly, nor should you expect to. We can learn to appreciate our beauty at every age and stage of life, regardless of the "gravity of the situation."

Words of Wisdom: Some fabulous technology can give us a real boost here. If you suffer from pelvic floor issues, ladies (and gentlemen), you don't need to. This technology mimics Kegels, only it can do so at a rate of 11,000 Kegels in a half-hour. That's waaaaay more than I can do even if I Kegeled my whole way through binge-watching *Grace & Frankie*.

"GRAVITY" —John Mayer
John Mayer's beautiful ballad is not about the
gravitational effects on our physical bodies; oddly enough,
some of the lyrics can be interpreted that way.

"GRAVITY IS A B*TCH" —Miranda Lambert
We might not like it, but gravity is a force to be reckoned with. Thank you for keeping it real, Ms. Lambert!

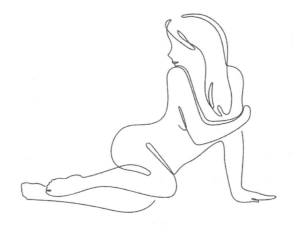

CHAPTER 19

Body Weight and Shape Changes

I often wonder what happened to the young girl who used to cry to her mom because she was so skinny and couldn't gain weight. Uh, yes, I am talking about myself. I was a slender young girl who carried that physicality into my 20s.

What I know now that I didn't realize then was that I was suffering from a mild form of body dysmorphia.

"Body Dysmorphic Disorder (BDD) describes a disabling preoccupation with perceived defects or flaws in appearance. It can affect all genders and makes sufferers excessively self-conscious." [15]

I suspect I still am struggling somewhat with body dysmorphia, but not about being skinny anymore, *au contraire*.

A statistic from *Parents* magazine tells us:

"Body dysmorphia for girls and boys starts at age 12-13, where 1 in 50 struggles with it. 60% of those struggles come from the girls and 40% from the boys." [16]

Whaaaat? This statistic is shocking, and it is disturbing to learn that our body image concerns start so early in life, as they did for me. I suspect most of us, at one time or another, have struggled with the angst of body dysmorphia.

In my pre-teen and teenage years, I wouldn't have been able to put a label of "dysmorphia" on my physical self-perception; I only knew how I felt about my body. Unsettled. Out of sorts. Thankfully, I wasn't in a state of full-blown criticality but just painfully aware, sensitive, and self-conscious about it. (But, boy, did I have a great tan. *Ha!*)

Body dysmorphia, however, can be a critical problem for people to deal with. I don't want my children, grandchildren, or yours, to deal with this. If you struggle or struggled with your body, no matter your age or gender, check out this fantastic free quiz from the *"Body Dysmorphic Disorder Foundation."* (QR code link is in Appendix B.) Please give it a go to see how you feel about your body today.

I took this test while drafting this book and was relieved that I scored extremely low now. I wonder how I might have scored as a young girl.

And today, let's just say I am no longer crying because I can't gain weight. My body weight, metabolism, and various body parts have shifted (Yes, *shift happens!*) because of the physical changes over the years. My midsection seems to be the ungrateful recipient. It also seems the dysmorphia has shifted, because now it's a struggle with my 64-year-old weight.

And speaking of physical and gravitational changes, do I even need to talk about what happens to our arms? If you know, you know. Ugggghhhh! If you don't know, ask your crazy Aunt Helen.

That said, I am eternally grateful that I have full mobility and use of my arms at this time—I do not take this for granted. If I must keep pumping a little iron to keep crazy Aunt Helen away, then I'm on it.

And don't even get me started on cellulite. Let's just normalize it already!

"Between 80% and 90% of all women who've gone through puberty have cellulite. Less than 10% of men have cellulite. Genetics, sex, age, the amount of fat on your body and your skin's thickness determine how much cellulite you have and how visible it is." [17]

Why does cellulite get so much attention when only 10-20% of the population doesn't have it? Why are we 80-90% club members so obsessed with it? Why are women made to feel so bad about it? WTF?

A brief PSA. [Based on the above cellulite statistic, I am not going to talk about why men seem to get yet another physical advantage over women. I could moan and groan over the unfairness of it, but it is just our reality.

That is a chromosomal and deoxyribonucleic acid discussion, which is way above my pay grade.

Additionally, I am not interested in man-bashing; that adds negative energy, and I do not want that for anyone.]

Anyways, because I could not gain weight as a younger woman, I couldn't understand why other women would fuss about their weight and how they had to diet to lose pounds. So I used to think, *"What's the big deal? You eat a few salads; you drop the weight, ba-da-boom, ba-da-bing."* I didn't know then what I know now, and I realize how fortunate I was to be in that physical state.

Nowadays, I need to think about what I eat. Despite my carefully curated meals and exercising, there doesn't seem to be enough counterbalance to offset my age and menopausal hormone changes. It is my reality—I'm *Not 20 Anymore*, and I have begrudgingly come to accept the physical changes that have come along in my life and how I look. I am learning to like, or at least accept, my curves. And I have let go of expecting to look like my daughter, who is half my age.

I have seen some mother/daughter photos with a 25-30-year age gap, and remarkably, there appears to be a slight difference between them visually. If that is your reality, I offer you my sincere congratulations for winning the gene pool lottery. *"You got it from your mama!"*

I eat well and exercise consistently to keep my body healthy and functioning as best I can. I must live with my genetic coding and accept the physical changes that my body has gone through. But I will not starve myself nor take up residence in the gym to regain my body from age 30.

At 64 years of age, I know I'm on the proverbial "other side of the hill," and I clearly understand that I am picking up speed on this side. Would I prefer to look like my 30-year-old self or even my 45-year-old self? Sure. Some days I would like to turn back the clock, but for the most part, no. I am content with where I am and choose to live healthfully and well, and I am not willing to only eat lettuce. Life is meant to be enjoyed.

It's a shame that we feel we must keep pushing back the hands of time on ourselves instead of treasuring who we are today.

"VICTORIA'S SECRET" —Jax
Jax nails it! Her lyrics are bold and brilliant. You need to listen to this. Is it true, *"Was Victoria made up by a dude?"*

"SCARS TO YOUR BEAUTIFUL" —Alessia Cara
Your anthem is a much-needed reminder that we don't need
to change ourselves to be beautiful. Thank you, Ms. Cara!

CHAPTER 20

You Are a Wonder Woman™

*I*t's time to take stock of the seemingly never-ending physical changes you already have bravely transitioned through. So let's quantify some of the adaptations your physical body has undergone. Don't worry; I'll go first!

As Cher sings, "If I Could Turn Back Time...." Yes, let's turn back time for a few minutes and consider what the hell happened to us along the way that might have contributed to our current body weight and shape. Ohhhhh, wait a minute, I know!

But do *you* remember all that you have encountered so far? Want to take a test to find out?

Good news: There are no wrong answers on this quiz. This is just for your personal knowledge. You can keep your score to yourself or share it with others because "Your Body = Your Call."

I invite you to participate in a quiz to calculate your Wonder Woman number ("WW#") at this time in your life. Add today's date and come back to it in a year or make a commitment to come back to it every year on your birthday to see if your score has changed.

Please don't come after me if I missed something. This is most likely a partial list, as these are just some of the things I have experienced so far. Feel free to add to it.

Incidentally, this is not a scientific calculation, so I also acknowledge that some of these physical adjustments and changes might deserve more weighting or value than the "1 point" scoring system. For now, let's keep it simple.

How to calculate your WW#:

1. For "Menstruation," add 1 point total, not 1 for each month. Please use this same scoring system for your "PMS" score. (*If you were counting each month, by the time you are in menopause, your score would be something like 480 points!*)
2. Add 1 point for each child. (I had two children, so I get 2 points). My daughter had 3 children, so she would get 3 points, etc.
3. Add 1 point for *each* additional major physiological life-altering event you might have experienced but that is not shown on the list. You can write those in the "Other" sections.
4. Total your points.

WONDER WOMAN QUIZ

Date: _____

To date, as a woman, I have experienced the following physical "modifications:"

_____ Menstruation

_____ Pre-menstrual syndrome (PMS)

_____ Pregnancy (x number of children)

_____ Childbirth (x number of children)

_____ Breastfeeding (x number of children)

_____ Post-pregnancy weight gain that lingered (1 point/pregnancy)

_____ Postpartum depression (1 point/pregnancy)

_____ Other "lingering" post-natal (birth) physical body changes (1 point each)

_____ Perimenopause menstrual cycle changes

_____ Hot flashes and/or night sweats

List other menopausal symptoms/body changes (add 1 point for each):

_____ Other _____

_____ Other _____

_____ Other _____

_____ Hormone replacement therapy (HRT) or other menopausal therapies

_____ Menopause or post-menopause

_____ Pelvic floor changes (resulting in incontinence, prolapse, etc.)

_____ Cellulite

_____ Gravitational changes to my triceps/arms

_____ Other physical gravitational changes not mentioned above (1 point each)

_____ Mood swings fuelled by hormonal changes of the above (1 point each)

_____ Other _____

_____ Other _____

_____ Other _____

_____ **My Total Wonder Woman Score = WW#**

"Women are the "weaker sex" —yeah, right."

The WW# represents the significant physical modifications that most women will (or could) experience just because we have XX chromosomes. It is our reality.

Each of these is life-altering, yet a woman's body is an immensely strong yet intricate *objet d'art* that adjusts to each change that comes along. These changes build up and, not surprisingly, take a progressive toll on our physical bodies.

Yet, as we move through these life stages and physical changes, our bodies consistently adapt.

"A change in the shape of the body creates
a change in the state of the soul."

—ARISTOTLE

As women, we are pretty remarkable specimens, aren't we? Most physiological changes that occur throughout our lives support the act of giving life, should we choose that path. Our physiology also signals us when that timeline has ended by putting us into a menopausal state.

I would never trade the experience of giving birth to my two children in exchange for my pre-natal body. My children were the greatest gifts I have ever received, and even if I weighed twice what I do right now because of that, I would gladly do so.

I get to decide what I want to look and feel like and how I present myself to the world. It is not a decision for others to make for me. Instead, I set all the parameters for that. My Body = My Call. Same for you.

I believe every woman has the right to make independent decisions to support her body. Own it!

As a 64-year-old, I have accepted that my body has lived a big part of its life. I had two children, I worked professionally for over 40 years, and I have soldiered through some challenging times, so if a few extra pounds are hanging around, so be it. Things could be much worse. I am incredibly fortunate to enjoy good health. And to my way of thinking, *good health trumps weight every time*.

As I have gone through life's stages and all the ups and downs, I have gained more confidence in who I am, what I stand for, and what I value. All of this has had a positive effect because it outweighs (pun intended) my feelings about my weight and body shape. I am still a work in progress in this space, and I suspect I always will be. I think that's good because I still care about how I present myself to the world. I am caring for myself and doing my reasonable best.

My current WW# sits at 23, but I am pretty confident that I will have a few more future physical modifications that will increase my WW status as I go forward in life. I don't know what the future holds for me, so I choose not to dwell on it and instead focus on what I can do right now.

I have morphed into a different sense of myself since I retired just three years ago and have a calmer acceptance of my physical presence when I consider my WW# and age.

Would I like to be ten pounds lighter? Yes, of course. Am I going to deprive myself of some great food, wine, cheese, and dark chocolate to do so? Absolutely not. But like everything, I have learned it has to be in moderation. I'm not perfect. I slip up; just watch me with a bag of Lays™ Dill Pickle Potato Chips!

You have heard this before... We all need to love the skin we are in. And I know how hard that can be. I have an ongoing love/hate relationship with my physical self and my self-body image, but I can also say that love far surpasses hate these days.

I also have learned some excellent skills along the way that have helped me through the years. I will share some of them in Part VI. I wish I knew then what I know now.

Words of Wisdom: We must give ourselves grace about our physical bodies, no matter what state our bodies are in. The point of the "Wonder Woman Quiz" was to make you take a minute to revisit what you have physically gone through up to this point in your life. It is extraordinary, and so are YOU. You have more strength than you can imagine, just for the physicality alone. You *are* a Wonder Woman! Go see how good you look in that cape?

"To call women the weaker sex is a label;
it is man's injustice to women.

If strength means brute strength, then a
woman is less brute than a man.

*If strength means moral power, then a
woman is immeasurably man's superior.*

*Has she not greater intuition, is she not more
self-sacrificing, has she not greater powers of
endurance, has she not greater courage?*

Without her, man could not be.

*If non-violence is the law of our being,
the future is with women.*

*Who can make a more effective appeal
to the heart than women?"*

—MAHATMA GANDHI

"IF I COULD TURN BACK TIME" —Cher
Wouldn't we all love a few do-overs? I would only turn back
time if I could take the wisdom I now have back with me.

"RISE UP" —Andra Day
Her message is a much-needed reminder that
you are stronger than you think. Thank you for
empowering us to keep fighting, Andra Day!

"MAN, I FEEL LIKE A WOMAN" —Shania Twain
This is a powerful song from one of our Canadian icons
and it will put you into your Divine Feminine zone. Grab
your hairbrush and sing along with Shania. As a Canadian,
I feel it would be impolite not to. *Let's go, girls!"*

CHAPTER 21

Changed!

"Change is the only constant."

—HERACLITUS

PART II SUMMARY

Indeed, the physical changes I have listed will likely resonate with you. This is what I have gone through so far, and I'm still alive and kickin'.

It is true when Ms. Mae West said, *"Growing old is not for the faint of heart."* It certainly is not. Let's quickly review the following:

- I know my WW# has nowhere to go but up. I have convinced myself that going "up" is usually exciting, right?
- I have learned that it takes a lot of grit and humility for a woman to weather the menopausal journey. The NIA says

"7-14" years, but who's counting? Every single pre- and post-menopausal woman is counting; that's who! And after reading this, so are their partners.

- I have come to accept who I am physically as best I can. Sometimes I get p*ssed off with myself when the scale moves the wrong way, but I tuck into some dill pickle chips or dark chocolate and get over it.

- I get to set my own physical body parameters. I don't allow anyone to influence me anymore. It's my decision. It's your decision, too.

- I don't heavily fall prey to the magazine or online images of other women and compare myself to them. I admire these women who look the way they do, whatever their age is. Assuming it's not all Photoshopped? And I happily look at magazine covers featuring women over 50. It is lovely when "*Not 50 Anymore*" women are featured—ditto for brand advertising for clothing and consumable items. More of this, please!

- I recently took an online eye test and was surprised to see what my presbyopic vision "prescription" now is. It had shifted up two levels in "reader-eyewear-speak." It surprised me. At this rate, in a couple of years, I will need to get a professional prescription again for glasses—it will feel like a throwback to Grade 6. But I can manage any "four-eyes" taunts that come my way now. I'm a Wonder Woman!

- I will continue my skincare regimen and use SPF diligently when I'm out in the sun. Please do the same for yourself, no matter your age.

- I keep my mind active and engaged in all sorts of ways. I will continue to level up as much as I can, but I don't feel obligated to read *War and Peace* (Leo Tolstoy) to be one of the "cool" kids. I am comfortable making independent decisions and may read it someday if it appeals to me.
- Incidentally, I have read *50 Shades of Grey* (E.L. James); why wouldn't I? (*wink, wink*). It's also my hair colour.

I am clear that more is coming my way, but I can only live in the here and now. I intend to make the best of it.

WHY DOES AGING SUCK?

Changes

EMOTIONAL EDITION

BACKGROUND FOR PART III:

Here's where some real ass-kickin' comes our way. I have to say these are in the top five (meaning, the worst of all). I would even go so far as to suggest that some of these things can eclipse the humility of a public hot flash.

I'm going to talk about the following:

- Ageism
- Invisibility
- Haters

So why do we need to deal with this kind of sh*t at this stage in our lives? Aren't these supposed to be our best years?

If you are under 50, I will paint some realism into your abstract and distracted mind (no offense). I say "abstract" because although you've heard of these issues, you probably think they won't happen to you. I had the same abstract opinion. They were some vague, theoretical problems "over there."

And I say "distracted" because I was distracted with my own life, family, work, and other issues, just as you likely are.

Sincerely, I hope it doesn't happen to you. But the odds are not in your favour. So let's get real.

If you are over 50, you might already know what I am talking about, particularly if you are of the feminine persuasion. But this is not an exclusive club for females; this is for everyone over 50.

These things sneak up on you and take you by surprise. It sucks!

Not only have I learned about these "things" as I experienced them, but most importantly, I learned how to recover from them. I don't want to be a victim during my 3rd Trimester of Life; that would be living with negative energy that I don't want for myself or anyone.

As I did in the "Aging Sucks: Physical Edition," I will offer you potential suggestions should you ever find yourself a target of ageism, invisibility, or haters. Feel free to consider them, modify them, or leave them. You do you.

CHAPTER 22

Ageism

*Although I am older now, it still seems like
I am running against the wind...*

I f all the physical implications of why I believe Aging Sucks are not enough, I have discovered that the most insulting "suck" of all is ageism, both society's perceptions and even our self-perceptions of aging.

It is also not lost on me that even my book title, "*Aging Sucks*," can be perceived as a negative stereotype about getting older. Please understand that I was quite deliberate in choosing this title, as the physical markers for a woman do suck.

I also deliberately chose to balance it by adding, *"But You're Gonna Love It!"* I am speaking my truth and never intended to insult anyone with my book title. I, too, have been a victim of ageism, inner and outer. Have you?

I realize ageism can extend to both ends of the spectrum, but I am referring to ageism for those past middle age.

I never thought much about ageism when I was 30 or 40. But when people started calling me *"ma'am"* and not *"miss,"* it seemed to be a sign that my age was beginning to show. Am I right? Has this happened to you?

I understand that people who have addressed me this way are trying to be respectful, but it was an aging marker for me, nonetheless.

Now, I am more than flattered when someone calls me *"Miss."* Yes, it still happens sometimes, and I always give that server a bigger tip. (So, heads-up to anyone in the hospitality industry.)

I suspect most of us only think of ageism when impacted by it.

Aging is tough, but what society thinks about aging is even more challenging and contributes to ageism. Here is Merriam-Webster's dictionary definition of *"ageism"*:

"Prejudice or discrimination against a particular age group, especially the elderly." [18]

Even the above dictionary definition is insulting; *"the elderly."* Sheeesh! I am even showing an ageism bias by saying that I don't consider myself a part of the "elderly," but it is a label with a negative connotation.

So, I looked up Merriam-Webster's definition of *"elderly."* Here it is:

"1: rather old especially being past middle age

2: of, relating to, or characteristic of later life or elderly persons" [19]

"Rather old?" Ouch! But their definition of "elderly" hits a little closer to home for me.

I am past middle age, but I still don't consider myself "elderly." I don't know when that stage will come, but I can say it is not right now. I suspect most people past middle age, which today is about 40-50 years old, never use that label for themselves. Do they? Do you?

I believe that Merriam-Webster utilized the word "elderly" without intending to insult everyone who has passed the middle-age mark. I also acknowledge that since I have endured the sting of ageism, I am sensitive.

To my Merriam-Webster editors: Should you change the above definitions, you might also want to acknowledge that ageism is not just for the elderly. Ageism goes the other way, too! Many people get judged and measured by their age as a sole criterion. Someone very young may not be respected for their ideas, despite their brilliance and originality.

As I waded deeper into this, I discovered that there are four distinct types of ageism, as defined by Dr. Robert Butler, President & CEO of the International Longevity Centre, U.S.A. He has described them as follows:

1. *"Personal Ageism*

Ideas, attitudes, beliefs, and practices on the part of individuals that are biased against persons or groups based on their age.

- *Our attitudes about old age are learned as children as we witness how those around us react to it. There is also the influence of television show characters and media messages. Whether positive or negative, we will be significantly influenced by these external factors and will apply these attitudes to others and our own aging process.*

2. *"Institutional Ageism*

- *Missions, rules, and practices that discriminate against individuals and/or groups because of their age.*
- *Ageism is also found in the workforce. As America turned from an agricultural to an industrial society, people looked at employment as a zero-sum equation: for every older person in the workforce, one younger person was kept from entering it. This wasn't and still isn't true. However, during the Great Depression when jobs were scarce, this zero-sum thinking led to mandatory retirement. There are few exceptions for mandatory retirement today, although some employers still hold ill-conceived perceptions about older workers. Most of us would rather retire than be forced out of employment based on our age.*

3. *"Unintentional Ageism*

- *Ideas, attitudes, rules, or practices that are carried out without the perpetrator's awareness that they are biased against persons or groups based on their age.*

- *Much of the ageism experienced in everyday life is unintentional—also called implicit bias. Ageism crept its way into the fabric of our society by using things such as humour to become something that has been widely accepted, things like over-the-hill birthday cards, and senior moments are examples.*

4. *"Intentional Ageism*

   - *Ideas, attitudes, rules, or practices that are carried out with the knowledge that they are biased against persons or groups based on their age.* [20]
   - *Intentional ageism includes carrying out practices that take advantage of the vulnerabilities of older persons. Scam artists are a good example of people who prey upon the vulnerabilities of older adults."* [21]

Not hiring someone based on older age is also intentional ageism and is against the law. Under the Age Discrimination Act in the United States, *"It is illegal to discriminate against job applicants who are age 40 or older."* [22]

Canada's provisions prohibiting age discrimination are grounded in the Charter of Rights and Freedoms (the "Charter"), which applies to all jurisdictions and governmental entities. Section 15(1) of the Charter contains this equality clause:

"Every individual is equal before and under the law and has the right to the equal protection and equal benefit of the law without discrimination and, in particular, without discrimination based on race, national or ethnic origin, colour, religion, sex, age or mental or physical disability." [23]

The Canadian Charter does not specify age, as the U.S. Age Discrimination Act does.

The United States Age Discrimination in Employment Act (ADEA) of 1967 reads:

"ADEA protects certain applicants and employees 40 years of age and older from discrimination on the basis of age in hiring, promotion, discharge, compensation, or terms, conditions or privileges of employment." [24]

In his report: "Barriers to the Labour Force Participation of Older Workers in Canada," published in May 2022 by the Fraser Institute, Morley Gunderson (renowned Canadian labour economist) writes:

"There are still barriers to older Canadians finding employment.… There is outright age discrimination, which is not taken as seriously as other forms of discrimination. People are living longer and very often retiring or being retired from their primary job, and they often want to keep on working, especially in a phased fashion." [25]

It would therefore seem that ageism is one of the most accepted forms of discrimination.

The World Health Organization has conducted extensive research on ageism. I will refrain from regurgitating this work, but I suggest you visit this material online if interested. My intention is to bring awareness to the fact that ageism is considered a global challenge by the United Nations. This problem has been around for a long time, and it appears it is not going away anytime soon.

We should start to find ways to normalize aging more. And not fight it so much. Wouldn't we all be so much more chill? It begins with each one of us.

Sam Cooke sings, "A Change is Gonna Come." I say, "A change has gotta come."

Words of Wisdom: To the best of my knowledge, I don't believe there is a one-size-fits-all solution for the distinct types of ageism. I also acknowledge that until it happens to you, it won't be easy to articulate how it might make you feel and what you will need to do to deal with it.

It felt like a kick to the gut; it challenged my sense of self-worth and how I perceived myself. It showed me that there was a disconnect between how I viewed myself and how some others had come to view me.

The first time it happened, it forced me into some significant self-reflection about where I was in my life; it was a reckoning. The gift from it is that this enlightenment eventually forced me to put a higher level of relevance and expedience into solidifying my future life and plans.

I went deep into journalling and wrote through the pain and shame. But that pain eventually became my gain. But, despite the emotional blow, it ultimately turned out to be a silver lining, paving the way for my future with a renewed sense of deliberateness and excitement. And it bolstered my motivation to write this book.

"AGAINST THE WIND" —Bob Seger & The Silver Bullet Band
This song tells us that age may bring challenges, but
we need to keep moving forward, against the wind.

"FIGHT SONG" —Rachel Platten
This is an empowering song to listen to when
you want to take back your life and prove to
yourself that you're going to be all right.

"A Change is Gonna Come" —Sam Cooke
This song was released in 1964 in support of the Civil Rights Movement, and I have no intention of minimizing that connection; sadly, it is still relevant today.

It strikes me that a change still needs to come along to end all forms of discrimination, including ageism.

CHAPTER 23

Invisibility

Where did I go?

R aise your hand if you have ever felt INVISIBLE. I see you. I do. You are not alone. I have been there and suffered the sting, and I am sorry you had to come up against it. I empathize with how that made you feel.

I was 58 years old when I had my first experience with invisibility. I know what it is like to feel as though I wasn't there while chatting with a group of people, all of them younger than myself. I felt dismissed and became immediately and painfully aware of my new irrelevance to them. *Ouch!* If we had taken a group "selfie" at the time, I would have been "Casper" and not even seen in the photo.

Dr. Robert N. Butler would label my situation as *"unintentional ageism."* As a woman living through the aging process, I called it a "punch to the throat." It came as a big old reality check—emphasis on the word "old."

I am not going to lie—it hurt—a lot. I was struck with emotions like hurt, anger, fear, and shame. Yes, I felt ashamed for getting older because it felt like "younger = relevant" and "older = no longer relevant."

I used to be relevant to most of the people in that group, and now, not so much. I know I am not in a unique position here. It happens to men and women alike. If this has happened to you, do you recall how it made you feel?

Despite invisibility being such a hard pill to swallow, I was eventually strong enough to rise above it. I had been through much bigger ego hits before. I understand that my responsibility is to manage my emotions and reactions to what others might say or do to me.

I needed to deal with those big feelings. So I did what has worked for me many other times. I purged the emotions, and I journalled my way through them. And I allowed myself to cry.

I got angry and held my *"IV Therapy"* conversations (Part VI, Chapter 40) with the perpetrators. I am sure they didn't even realize they were doing it, and I did not feel it was a deliberate snub, but it hurt, nonetheless.

When we were kids, if my siblings and I did something not using our intelligence (which I seem to recall was quite often), my mother would say, "*Bless your empty heads*" to us. So, I remembered that; I forgave them and blessed my younger friends' empty heads.

Initially, the sting of invisibility sucks big time. How you present and are accepted in this world is your essence, your sense of self and worth. It. Is. You.

It is one of those lifetime gut-wrenchers. As Ross Geller would scream in one of those classic "*Friends*" episodes[26], this was a huge "pivot point" (can you hear me screaming "*pivot?*") that you must traverse in coming to terms with your age and your sense of self-esteem.

In all honesty, I had felt this lack of relevance sneaking up on me for a few years before my retirement, but I had chosen to ignore it instead of taking the time (ahead of time) to prepare myself before I had to confront it. My bad. I knew it was coming; it was inevitable. I had watched the same movie play out throughout 30 years of my professional life to numerous colleagues ahead of me.

I had read retirement books, attended corporate retirement planning seminars, and used online corporate wellness educational resources. I am not calling this book "Aging for Dummies" because I wasn't a dummy; I knew all this was coming. Yet I chose to have my eyes wide shut on this one.

I'm not blaming anyone but myself. *I'm Not 20 Anymore*. But, despite all the evidence to the contrary, I still didn't think it would happen to me. Or maybe I thought it wouldn't happen until I was 100.

I thought I had become good at not noticing (or choosing not to notice) that I used to be one of the young'uns who had enjoyed a solid history at work through my career accomplishments.

At the risk of coming across as someone intending to blow smoke, I was one of those sought out for advice, guidance, and career direction, and I am so proud to have been a part of so many successful careers along the way.

But I was being approached with the *"So, when are you gonna retire?"* questions more often than the *"Have you got a minute?"* questions.

Once I recovered from the jarring emotional wake-up through self-shaming, anger, embarrassment, and guilt for getting older and becoming invisible, I knew I needed to redefine it and look at it through a different lens. So I started to vigorously push myself forward in a completely new direction. I pivoted.

I transmuted my self-deprecating thoughts into *"Get going in this game of life"* thoughts. It was the jolt I needed… and I finally realized that my life was not a dress rehearsal.

My career, as good (or bad) as it was, was. I finally admitted to myself that I was tired of working such long hours, and those repeated *Mad Max*[27] drives back and forth on the Trans-Canada Highway were losing their appeal.

I got honest with myself and stitched down a retirement date, no longer making it nebulous. I was the only one who knew my retirement plan. All that counted was that the gears were set in motion mentally for me, which was the biggest hurdle in accepting my waning commercial relevance.

I also have learned that "invisibility" is a Superpower. Through time and a lot of reflection and self-drive, I learned to take advantage of that new level of power and strength that my invisibility cloak has given me. On my terms. I can choose when to be visible and when I choose to be invisible. Knowing I can decide this is so empowering.

I'll share a secret with you: I have been wearing my invisibility cloak the entire time I've drafted this book. I haven't even told my children. Why? I just wanted to see if I had it in me to be this authentic and vulnerable during my transition into my 3rd Trimester of Life.

I will tell you that when I put on my invisibility cloak, I get so much accomplished and feel so empowered. I dare myself to do something different. Get your own invisibility cloak, if you don't already have one, and decide when to wear it and when to hang it in your closet. Take advantage of this Superpower you never even knew you had.

Words of Wisdom: If you have ever felt the sting of invisibility or been a victim of ageism because of your advancing age and/or if you are struggling to accept all the emotions that came along with it, consider doing what I did.

1. Deal with those feelings and emotions first. Cry them out, shout them out, write them out, act them out (you get the idea) when you have the time and emotional capacity to unpack them.
2. Come to a place of acceptance. This might take some time; give yourself the grace and the space to work through it.
3. Forgive those who made you feel that way. Whether they did it

intentionally or not. Follow my mom's advice: *"Bless their empty heads!"* The forgiveness is for you, not for them. It releases the negative mental attachment.

4. Make peace with it. You must do this before accepting and moving on from what happened. (Take a peek at Part VI, Chapter 40, for some DIY ideas about forgiveness.)

Words of Wisdom: Take advantage of your invisibility. Own it. Think about what you would like to do while wearing your invisibility cloak. Here are some ideas:

- Keep levelling up. Stay as relevant as you can—for yourself and your loved ones.
- Keep moving, singing, dancing, online learning, and dating (if you're doing that).
- Try new things, new restaurants, new foods, and new wines.
- Get rid of old things that no longer bring you joy. Do this with people too! If they no longer bring you joy, then you know what to do.
- Go on adventures; travel to new places or revisit your favourites.
- Brush up on your second-language skills or learn a new language. Duolingo™ is free and fabulous. (See Appendix B.) Did you know the word "sexagenarian" in French is "sexagenaire?" *Trés sexy, n'est-ce-pas?*
- Do volunteer work, start a creative project (write a book?), or get another job after retirement.
- Go out and meet new friends or reconnect with long-time friends.
- If you can afford it, buy the better wine for yourself. Seriously.

- Glow up. Treat yourself to a spa treatment. Take care of yourself.
- Be as good to yourself as you can be. You deserve it.
- Do whatever you want. You have the eye of the tiger.
- Stop caring what others think…. Ain't your business anyways. Don't look for validation from others. Find it within yourself.
- Step into your power. Build your self-confidence.
- Don't play small. Take up space.
- Let your light shine, and your voice be heard.
- Be authentic. Don't hold yourself back.
- Lean into your age, wisdom, self-worth, and beauty, just as you are right now. You have earned your stripes through your tour of duty.
- Become visible or invisible on your terms. You get to decide this. It's like breathing in, breathing out, waxing on, waxing off (remember *The Karate Kid*?) You'll get better at this with practice, I promise.
- Step in front of your mirror again and do some *Mirror, Mirror* work when you need to. (See Part VI, Chapter 39). Remind yourself that you are beautiful.

"Confidence isn't walking into a room and thinking you're better than everyone…. It's walking in and not comparing yourself to anyone at all."

—AUTHOR UNKNOWN

Here are some songs to help you move, groove, and start to find yourself again:

"INVISIBLE" —Hunter Hayes
I have lived his lyrics, and so I resonate with this song.
I honestly hope you are never made to feel invisible.

"CRY TO ME" —Solomon Burke
If you're going to cry, cry to this fine gentleman.
Just sayin'! This one will put you into your "Dirty Dancing" feelings. It is divine. You're welcome.

"BEAUTIFUL" —Christina Aguilera
You are beautiful, just the way you are. Thank you
for this uplifting message, Ms. Aguilera.

"JUST THE WAY YOU ARE" —Bruno Mars
He's right… you are amazing right now, exactly as you are!

"ROAR" —Katy Perry
Take your power back. Roaarrrrr!

CHAPTER 24

Haters Gonna Hate

efore I go on, I feel compelled to address something I, unfortunately, have seen repeatedly.

Seeing how other women rip into each other on social media (SM) platforms is appalling. I see younger women attacking and bashing mature women for their decisions about everything, from their physical appearance and clothing choices to their cosmetic applications.

If that isn't enough, I have seen younger women viciously attack women over 40 by commenting that they are too old to be on some SM apps and don't belong there. *Whaaaat?* Their public bashing has left some women in tears. This is "intentional ageism," if you need to put a label on it, and I'm calling out these younger women for just being *mean*.

So, let me take it upon myself to address all the "mean girls" out there who felt it was their place to attack other women on SM platforms:

Please stop serving up your unsolicited critiques of other women. Doing that is never a good look on you. You are embarrassing yourself... big time. And what goes around comes around, girl. Trust me; you don't wanna mess with Karma.

Why not take the energy you've used bullying and verbally abusing other women and invest that time instead into figuring out why your self-esteem is so low? I have been around long enough to learn and understand that hurt people hurt people. So please do the work on this. It is worth it. You are worth it.

You have to allow real grown-ass women to decide what they want to wear. These women are also mature and responsible enough to know which SM platforms they wish to participate in. Trust me; when these women choose to step up into their Divine Masculine vibe like I am right now, they will ask for your opinion if they want it. They will also tell you their opinion of your "interest" in them.

Or, to put it another way, if you don't have something nice to say, say *nothing* instead of saying something hurtful. Take the high road.

None of us are covered with bulletproof coating. Words can hurt and inflict damage that can be difficult to overcome. Be kind to one another. We sisters need to have one another's backs, join ranks, and support each other. We are all part of the same club. And we are all connected because we aren't getting any younger.

Women need to band together to support and uplift one another, not make sniper attacks on one another, particularly as it relates to aging. We are each responsible for treating one another with mutual respect, dignity, and kindness to change the narrative on aging for women collectively.

I don't want my daughter or granddaughters to continue dealing with this garbage as they age. Do you? As a society, we can do better.

And as women, I know we can do better.

> *"Together, all of us are more powerful than any one of us."*

Words of Wisdom: If you have been a target of online bullying:

- I suggest you take a stand. I am not recommending that you have to get into an e-fight with the bully but stand up for yourself. Do it with integrity, grace, and forgiveness. Yes, forgive the bully. That's for both of you.
- Or walk away from it and don't engage your bully, block them, unfriend them, leave the group or whatever you need to do, but make sure you don't carry it around inside of you. Remind yourself that people's behaviour is a direct reflection of their wounds, and they are projecting onto you how they feel about themselves.
- I would also invite you to consider this:

> *"There are 7.92 billion people in the world. Why are you letting one of them ruin your life?"*

To the women who have been a bully (even a little bit):

- Know that these "sucky" things will happen to you as you go down your life's path. Aging is universal; you will not be given a "Hall Pass."
- Enjoy your beauty, youth, and vitality. Learn about your Divine Feminine (DF) and Divine Masculine (DM) energies and how and when to deploy them. (See Part V, Chapter 34.) Learn how to love yourself, too.
- Practice self-care. Be prepared for what is coming in your life as you have more trips around the sun. Educate yourself. Please familiarize yourself with what is coming because I promise you it is coming.
- We are living in very fast-changing and, sometimes, bewildering times. Be smart. Stay open-minded. I encourage you to take wise advice from any other woman who has "been there."
- I wish I had known more about which questions to ask about the aging process and what to expect, but I didn't. I was just like you, and growing old wasn't for me at the time. I was young, vibrant, and infallible, just like you feel right now.
- Be the woman who chooses to fix another queen's crown without telling her. Be the woman who tells another woman that she has lipstick or spinach on her teeth, not publicly nor with cruel intent, but with a genuine intention to help.

Madeline Albright, former U.S. Secretary of State, said:

"There is a special place in hell for women
who do not help other women."

Extend kindness and compassion; that is a good look on anyone.

"You never know who in the crowd, standing beside
you in line or passing you in the street, might
be raised in spirit, or even lifted from despair,
by the kindness in your glance or the comfort
of your smile. But they may never forget."

—MIKE DOOLEY

"MEAN" —Taylor Swift

Play this song when you feel like someone was mean to you.
You'll know when you need this. Why they gotta be so mean?

"Forgive them and *bless* their empty heads!"

"SHAKE IT OFF" —Taylor Swift
Do what she says and shake the haters off. Tell me you
don't feel better right away when you play this song.

"STRONGER" —Kelly Clarkson
What doesn't kill you does make you stronger.
Take your power back. Alexa: Repeat.

CHAPTER 25

The Silver Lining

PART III SUMMARY

Some of the emotional experiences I endured were brutal. They forced me to make an internal visit to myself to regain my footing and to start building a new foundation within myself... ultimately, a stronger one.

I healed from them and learned and transformed from them. So will you. Just don't keep the pain and shame inside.

> *"It's funny how, when things seem the darkest,*
> *moments of beauty present themselves*
> *in the most unexpected places."*
>
> —KAREN MARIE MONING

It's true—there is a silver lining in every cloud, and sometimes you must work through the grey to find it, but it will be there. I will tell you how I learned to find it in Parts V and VI.

Branding, Boomers, and Beauty

BACKGROUND FOR PART IV:

I will explain more fully why I have chosen to categorize our lives into Trimesters by age. There's not much mystery here, as I have laid it out already, but I'll let you know why I refer to them this way.

I will highlight and gush over some of our leading Hollywood ladies and how they are challenging the status quo about women and aging. Lead on, ladies! You have our attention.

I will also share some fascinating demographics and statistics about aging. Some juicy tidbits will be worth learning about, especially if you are involved in sales, advertising, consumer goods manufacturing, design, or marketing. Boom!

CHAPTER 26

Life's Trimesters

*I*n researching material for this book, I came across a TED talk by Jane Fonda in 2011.[28] Do yourself a favour; click on the QR code in Appendix B and watch it. Though delivered eleven years ago, it is still relevant, provocative, and insightful.

Ms. Fonda's TED talk followed on the heels of her book titled *"Prime Time."*[29] Although I had watched Ms. Fonda's TED talk, I purposefully did not read her book until I was more than 95% of the way through writing my own, and even then, I chose to stop reading her book on page 47. Why, might you ask?

I didn't want to be so intimidated by her work that I couldn't even try to write about my feelings and ordeals with the aging process. Let me be clear here: I have Ms. Fonda on a bit of a pedestal. These are my insecurities surfacing.

I also didn't want to feel obligated to attempt to match her standard, her wisdom, and intelligence. In other words, I didn't want to get discouraged by reading her book and suffer from a severe case of "comparisonitis." Can you blame me? She's Jane Fonda!

When I ordered her book online, I was grateful that I had not read it ahead of time, or else I would have needed more courage and energy to write this book. Pretty cowardly, eh? But, here I am!

My journey has been different, and my approach to sharing my story differs, but there are some strong threads of familiarity between our unique journeys. But, of course, that shouldn't surprise me. Aging is universal, and as women, we have had many similar physical realities, even in our vastly different lives.

Ms. Fonda has divided the stages of aging into three categories: the 1st, 2nd, and 3rd Acts, brilliantly, as a nod to her acting career. I categorize them into Trimesters, where I have chosen to draw a parallel to the stages of birth and development.

Birth – Age 30	1st Trimester (T1)
Age 30 – 60	2nd Trimester (T2)
Age 60 – 90	3rd Trimester (T3)
Age 90+	Queenagers (Q)

So, why didn't I just use Ms. Fonda's 3-Act metaphor? I didn't want to steal her work or her thunder. Instead, she deserves a standing ovation for her work and how she is living and so brilliantly representing women in her 3rd Act of Life.

Ms. Fonda has said, *"Perhaps the task of our 3rd Act is to finish up the act of finishing ourselves,"* and in her TED talk, she expertly walks us through her analogy.

It felt like a new life started for me at age 60, not surprisingly when it coincided with my retirement. The 1st and 2nd trimesters of my life were the preparatory stages for me becoming who I am today.

I went through my 1st Trimester with excitement and naïveté, enjoying the bloom and freshness of my early years. As I look back, I can see that I ventured through my teen years and into my 20s, trying to get a handle on this thing called "life" and getting ready for what was to come. But I also remember that I thought I already knew it all. I know now how naïve I really was and how little I really knew.

My 2nd Trimester was a lot more work than my 1st, but the growth I experienced was phenomenal. I was getting more accustomed to myself and the changes life was bringing me, but I wasn't quite used to all the kicks I was getting, not to mention the physical and emotional changes. Like my 2nd Trimester of pregnancy, big-time growing pains happened in my 2nd Trimester of Life. Big-time lessons too.

Everything started to feel a bit easier in the latter part of the 2nd Trimester. I had learned how to deal with the surprises and "curve-balls" via some coping strategies I had developed and used along the way—ditto for my 2nd Trimester of pregnancy. I felt more confident and thought I had learned so much about myself.

I learned to build my Self-Care Toolkit based on my experiences, which I will share with you in Part VI and which I hope will continue to serve me in my 3rd Trimester.

Also, in the latter part of my 2nd Life Trimester, I started to prepare more actively for my "D-Day." Not my Delivery Date (as in pregnancy), and certainly not Doomsday, but my "Departure Date" (retirement). It was a refreshing and energizing change of perspective the closer it came.

The 3rd Trimester of my life has been the best since I entered the zone at 60. It feels as though my life has just started. I hope you will find it the same.

"FOREVER YOUNG" —Bob Dylan
For the purists. The lyrics say it all.

"FOREVER YOUNG" —Rod Stewart
May good fortune and a strong guiding light always
be with you. Thank you for this timeless message.

"NIGHT CHANGES" —One Direction
Does it drive you crazy how fast time flies?
One Direction understands that we are
all only getting older, baby!

CHAPTER 27

My Hollywood Heroines

I discovered that I had to come to my own rescue many times, and accepting the aging process has been no different. I hadn't come across any great cheerleaders until I started to look for them when I hit my 3rd Trimester of Life.

- I have always admired Betty White through the years, but watching her during her final years, I added her as a role model for my 3rd Trimester of Life. Throughout her life, she bedazzled us with her humour, grace, poise, and dignity until she passed away just 17 days short of her 100th birthday. Betty White has said,

  "Butterflies are like women; we may look beautiful and delicate, but baby, we can fly through a hurricane."

And didn't she live her words? What a remarkable woman.

- Jane Fonda says, *"We finish ourselves."*

- Jann Arden says she is in *"… the act of becoming someone I always hoped I would be…"* [30]

It is exciting to see that women over 50 years of age are being more prominently featured in cosmetic and beauty ads and not Photoshopped to try to appear younger.

- As I write this, *Sports Illustrated*™ just announced its 2022 Swimsuit Edition magazine cover… Ms. Maye Musk, at age 74, looks stunning—Bravo to the SI editors, and kudos to Ms. Musk.

- Did you see the incomparable Dame Helen Mirren in the May 9, 2022, edition of *People*™ magazine? At age 76, she is stunningly beautiful and on the cover of one of North America's most popular magazines. She doesn't call it beauty; she calls it "swagger." How fresh and invigorating is that? And yes, she does swagger well. And maybe a bit of saunter and strut as well. Love it!

- Jane Fonda, an 84-year-old, graced the cover of *Glamour*™ magazine in its May 2022 edition, where she was last on its cover in 1959. Glamorous indeed!

- Dame Emma Thompson gives us a fearless and beautiful performance in the movie *Good Luck to You, Leo Grande*. [31] What a powerful performance from a woman, aged 63, who personifies self-love and self-acceptance.

"I think one of the greatest tragedies in our lives—in women's lives—is the time, the effort, the energy, the passion that we've wasted on not being able to accept our own bodies."
—EMMA THOMPSON

- Oprah Winfrey continues to dazzle us at age 68, and Tina Turner and Cher are still rocking it at 82 and 76, respectively.

- And can we give a standing "O" to the ever-effervescent Jamie Lee Curtis, age 64, who is using her celebrity status to promote "pro-aging" and to stand up against "anti-aging"?

These are just a few famous women I greatly admire for many reasons, and there are many more. Whom do you admire?

"Anyone who keeps the ability to see beauty never grows old."
—FRANZ KAFKA

While I recognize there is still a long way to go to eclipse the ageism and invisibility phenomena, I feel: "A shift is happening." Do you feel it?

It starts with each of us!

"The beauty of a woman is not in the clothes she wears, the figure that she carries, or the way she combs her hair. The beauty of a woman is seen in her eyes, because that is the doorway to her heart, the place where love resides. True beauty in a woman is reflected in her soul. It's the caring that she lovingly gives, the passion that she shows and the beauty of a woman only grows with passing years."

—AUDREY HEPBURN

"YOU'RE BEAUTIFUL" —James Blunt
You're beautiful—it's true!

"LANDSLIDE" —Fleetwood Mac
Ms. Nicks' lyrics make us ask ourselves if we can navigate the shifting tides of life? Can we weather the changing seasons that come our way?

CHAPTER 28

Shift Happens

*S*tatistics show that we are living thirty years longer than our great-grandparents did. That's another entire trimester, folks. So I'll soon have to change my life cycle references from Trimesters to Quads.

"In 1950, Canada had 11.3% of its population aged 60 and over."

"In 2014, over 6 million Canadians were 65 or older, representing 15.6% of Canada's population.

"By 2030, seniors will number over 9.5 million and make up 23% of Canadians." [32]

Labour force data from Statistics Canada from the 2021 Census shows that 24% of Canadians 65 years and older are still working. That is up from our 2016 Census, when 22% of the 65+ age group were working.

The U.S. Bureau of Labor Statistics projects that *"the 65– to 74-year-old and 75+ age groups are projected to have faster labor force growth rates annually than any other age groups. Over the entire 2014–24 decade, the labor force growth rate of the 65–74-year-old age group is expected to be about 55%, and the 75+ age group is expected to be about 86%, compared with a 5% increase for the labor force as a whole."*[33]

The implications are far-reaching, and this major shift should make us consider re-evaluating negative societal stereotypes about aging. We are living longer because our health is better.

I decided to retire early and left at age 60, and I am incredibly fortunate to be in that position. I recognize, however, that many others are not in a place to do so, at least from a financial standpoint.

Bill VanGorder, Chief Operating Officer for the Canadian Association of Retired Professionals, says, *"People my age and older thought that they were planning for freedom 55, and after retiring, they're finding out they're living longer, and there's a huge fear that they're going to outlive their money."*[34]

Despite the Canadian Federal Government increasing Old Age Security benefits for Canadians aged 75 and older by 10% in July of 2022, some of our fellow Canadians will be challenged financially as they get older. It is a sobering problem.

These statistics tell us that women (and men) must build a deliberate and sustainable plan to prepare financially for their post-retirement years as early as possible. (See Part VII.)

Now, if I were still a marketer, I would be paying attention to these statistics; seniors will soon represent almost 25% of the population.

In Canada, in 2022, we are currently over 19%.

What will seniors want or need to purchase? I will not build a list for you (I'm retired.) I only want to make a point.

And if you don't believe anything I am saying here, then I recommend you check for yourself. Women over 50 on all social media platforms are asking for help.

To all brand marketers, consider being more inclusive in your advertising for women and men over 50. Review this excerpt from Adweek:

"As marketers, we must have our fingers on the pulse of the cultural conversation. We can't relegate this responsibility to someone else. It's our job to ensure our brand stays relevant and top of mind for our consumers.

"Anyone who touches a brand should listen and watch to see what's happening in our world daily. Ensure that someone in your marketing ecosystem is the designated keeper of cultural conversations and keep the rest of the team apprised at crucial moments." [35]

If you are a Canadian, you probably have heard about Lisa LaFlamme, an award-winning career journalist and former CTV National News anchor.

Mita Mallick, a Diversity and Inclusion thought leader, writes, *"A storm erupted on social media when beloved Canadian news anchor Lisa LaFlamme was allegedly ousted from her job. LaFlamme had worked for the network for over 35 years, winning awards for reporting from conflict and disaster zones.*

"According to reports, senior CTV News executive Michael Melling had asked who had approved the decision to 'let Lisa's hair go grey.' LaFlamme is no longer with CTV News, while Melling is taking a leave immediately." [36]

A storm erupted, indeed. Canadians were outraged. Lisa LaFlamme is a very respected professional woman, a household name in Canada. CTV News allegedly released her, presumably simply because she decided to no longer colour her hair without getting CTV News' approval.

CTV didn't even extend the courtesy of revealing her departure and honouring her legacy at the time of her release. Ms. LaFlamme had to announce her own departure on social media. She did so with pure vulnerability, authenticity, humility, and extreme bravery.

Literally translated, *"LaFlamme"* means "The Flame." Her dismissal from CTV News ignited a huge flame among Canadians. Both women and men immediately came to her defence; we were blowing up social media, and international major news outlets were also picking it up.

Did you notice how quickly Dove™ took the pulse of Canadians and responded? Within days, Dove switched out their iconic gold logo for grey as an act of solidarity and a voice against ageism.

So did Wendy's™. They switched Wendy's hair colour from red to grey in their famous logo.

Mita Mallick says, *"As this cultural moment took off, sparking debates about ageism and sexism in the workplace, Dove™ decided to enter the conversation swiftly. With its #KeepTheGrey Campaign, Dove did what brands often get wrong: showing up in a cultural moment relevant to the brand, the consumer, and the greater ecosystem.*"[37]

Leapfrogging off the Dove campaign, *#KeepTheGrey*, Canadians responded by changing our full-colour social media photos to grey versions in a visual show of solidarity with Ms. LaFlamme.

Ms. LaFlamme's courage to speak up and vulnerably share her story was a catalyst for bringing an avalanche of awareness to the discriminatory behaviour of ageism. It was terribly unfortunate that it came at the expense of Ms. LaFlamme's livelihood. Yet her reputation soared as a result of this. Talk about a silver lining.

Dove's *#KeeptheGrey* Campaign is a rock-solid example of cultural awareness, marketing with a conscience about growing cultural and demographic trends.

'Baby boomer' is a term used to describe a person born between 1946 and 1964. The term 'baby boomer' is derived from the boom in births that took place after the return of soldiers from WWII."[38]

Generally speaking, Boomers are the demographic group with the most money to spend, but isn't it odd that most advertising is geared primarily toward the younger generation? I am not discounting younger generations, and I fully understand that brand marketers are trying to hook them now to get them loyal to their brands at an early age. I get it. Yet, it would seem they are discounting us. Just sayin'.

I also think marketers should also be paying some attention to the generations on either side of the Boomers:

- The "Silent Generation" (people born between 1928–1945):
  - What are their needs and wants now and in the future?
  - Statistically speaking, we are all supposed to be living longer, so moving forward, there will be a lot more people who will have significant needs in their extended 'senior' years.
- The Gen Xers (people born between 1965–1980):
  - The Gen Xers are now well into their mid-life. For sure, they'll be living longer than their parents.
  - What do the Gen Xers want and need now and in the future?

Consider lumping two or all three of these generations into one category for your brand and marketing efforts. Zoomer Media has taken the leap forward on this:

> **"'Zoomers' are the 17.2 million Baby Boomers and Gen Xers over the age of 45 in Canada."**
>
> —MOSES ZNAIMER

Zoomers are thought to be the most powerful audience in Canada, and I daresay, the United States, as there are approximately 141 million Baby Boomers and Gen X'ers over 45 years old in the U.S. *Zoom… Zoom!*

The beauty industry preys on women's insecurities about their age and appearance. We are made to feel that looking younger gives us a higher currency in our social world.

But why not encourage women to choose how they want to look?

Why the constant message that looking younger and being thinner is better? Those expectations are unrealistic. Take a look around. Are you capturing and representing the real female demographic with your advertising efforts? This is us! Help us, and we will help you.

Brand marketers, in your advertising, please consider celebrating and featuring women and men over 50. We would love to see more real women of all shapes and sizes, including our Hollywood Heroines/Heroes over 50, on your magazine covers and within your content, especially without digital enhancement.

See women for who we really are at every age. Please don't make us feel like we all have to look like we did at 25. There are many reasons we don't want to go back there; women have physically, mentally, and emotionally evolved by the time we're in our midlife. Men, too, I suspect.

We like who we are and have already been through enough in life, so please don't make us feel bad because we're *Not 20 Anymore*. We are celebrating it so welcome to the party. We got it goin' on in a whole different way, baby!

Dove Unilever has done a great job featuring real women in its advertising. Mature women have developed some beautiful curves, and I suspect I am speaking on behalf of almost all female Zoomers that we relate to those women more than we do perfectly sculpted young hard bodies!

To all clothing manufacturers, stores, and brands, please consider people over 50 for your designs. We like to dress well in clothing made to work with and enhance our physical changes. Some of you get it, but many of you don't.

If Zoomers do fit your target demographic, how about featuring us in your advertising and branding portfolio?

The American Association of Retired Persons (AARP) indicates that:

"While more than a third of Americans are 50 and over, they appear in just 15% of media images. According to Havas Group, a measly 5% of advertising explicitly targets older consumers.

"There are 75 million Baby Boomers in the U.S., aged 57 and up, with combined spending of $548 billion per year. Behind them in purchasing power are GenXers (49 million citizens), who are dishing out $357 billion per year. It is leaps and bounds ahead of what millennials and GenZers have in their piggy banks.

"Baby Boomers are educated, intelligent, street smart, and can smell bullsh*t from a mile away. And we have money to spend on ourselves. Don't dismiss us." [39]

"ALL ABOUT THAT BASS" —Meghan Trainor
Photoshop ain't fooling me,
No more fake imagery,
Let's call it out and set it free.
Make it stop.

"FIREWORK" —Katy Perry
Ms. Perry's song reminds us that everyone is special and
has something unique to offer the world. Ignite the spark
within you and let it shine bright, like fireworks! *Boom!*

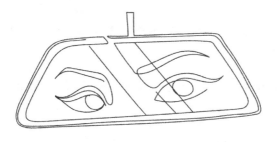

CHAPTER 29

My Rearview Mirror Musings

PARTS I–IV SUMMARY

I have covered a lot of the "Why Aging Sucks" elements, but mostly, it sucks because there is a fierce recognition that on that proverbial hill of life, I am on the other side of it. It's a high hard slap on the head, and that realization brings some sadness.

I question if I have done my best or done all I've wanted to do so far. I look at myself in the mirror differently, not just physically, but probingly. Did I do right by my children, family, friends, work colleagues, and my world?

Indeed, I have some regrets and would like to have the opportunity for a few do-overs, but mostly I have come to accept that I am where I am, and I cannot go backward.

I have come to look at my past much like I do when I hear World War I and World War II stories. I know there is absolutely nothing I can do to change the outcomes of those wars and their history in all their storied parts: the good, the bad, and the ugly. But we can learn from history.

Nothing I do now can change my past. It is what it is, and I have come to accept it, all of it.

I fully accept my past because it's in the history books now. I don't live there; I worked and played there and, more importantly, I learned there.

So, am I past my "Best Before Date"? I don't think so. I retired, but I have not expired.

I may not be as good at some things as I once was, but I live and love myself and my life just as I am. I am incredibly grateful for that.

I am trying to accept aging as gracefully and boldly as I can. What's the alternative? Live in misery? No, I am not going that route. I have spent some time in Miseryville and know it is sad and lonely.

I had to change my thinking about aging and my place on the "hill." It had to start with myself. It was a gradual acceptance. I haven't got this thing called 'life' nailed, not by a long shot. I am and will forever be a student and a work in progress. That is what makes it all so interesting.

I have packed up my life events and the wisdom I have gained, and I have chosen to move up to the penthouse level for the rest of my life. Not literally, but metaphorically. The air is cleaner, the perspective on my past is different, and I find the view so much better.

I have learned to slow things down and take in the whole view. I have mellowed, and I feel more grounded than ever before. I have earned my place here in the penthouse and have a good line of sight to my future from here. It's still off in the distance, but I know what's coming my way.

As I have aged, I have adopted a more cavalier attitude, a *"Meh!"* sort of thing. That attitude certainly didn't come overnight, but I have grown into it somehow.

I have fought aging and will continue to do what I can to keep myself vibrant, relevant, and healthy. I dyed my hair for years to keep my 50 shades of grey at bay. I could have been entirely silver at 45 (or earlier), so it took me a while to move away from the "dark side."

I am still fighting, or rather, slowing, some elements of the aging process but am letting Mother Nature win a few rounds, too. I have learned that it is easier to work with aging than to try and fight it every step of the way.

I don't want to spend my retirement years bemoaning my age and all the physical modifications accompanying it. I know my WW# will only increase as I get older. I realize that I have a sacred duty to take care of myself. I am choosing to live my life and squeeze as much as I can from my 3rd Trimester of Life. I have come to realize that aging is a gift, so I choose to be a beneficiary, not a victim.

"Aging is not so much about adding years to your life;
instead, it is about adding more life to your years."
—DR. EDWARD STIEGLITZ

Think about that for a few minutes. Don't negatively stereotype yourself about your age. Instead, reframe it and take personal responsibility for yourself.

> *"Now is the best time to assess whether the lenses in our aging attitude need an adjustment. It is well worth our time. A positive attitude toward aging can add 7.5 years to one's life."*
>
> —DR. BECCA LEVY

Make your own decisions about your appearance, feelings, self-esteem, values, and what you believe in and stand for. You know what feels authentic to you. Lean into your true essence, no matter your age.

I am happy to share what I have learned based on my learnings and research. But I acknowledge I am still learning, don't have all the answers, and certainly don't know all that is in store for me as I take more trips around the sun. The best and worst are yet to come. I am preparing and will be as ready as I can be. What's the option? I will not wallow in self-pity because of my age, looks, and future. I don't want to live with that energy for the rest of my life.

I imagine if Oprah Winfrey were to ask me her famous interview question: *"What do you know for sure?"* that today, I would answer her, *"I have learned that aging is not all about loss and decline, far from it. Aging is an opportunity we should welcome with open arms."*

I have learned to embrace and fully accept my current age. I suggest you try to do the same. Lean into it. It feels that I now really "get it" and that time has become a more precious commodity now that I no longer take for granted. I also have learned that time does seem to move faster as you age. Fridays seem to come much quicker than they used to, as does the holiday season.

I am grateful for the cards that life has dealt me so far. I wouldn't have said so while holding some of those cards. I remember feeling sad, broken, ashamed, regretful, and scared sometimes.

And there were times when I wasn't even sure I wanted to come out of the dark. But there was a pull inside of me, my internal pilot light, that I had to ignite. And I did. At the risk of over-dramatizing, I have had to lift myself out of the ashes. I have been a Phoenix several times.

You will have dark times in your life. Know, however, that your dark times will pave the way for your best learnings in life. My strongest advice would be to not go through any dark period of your life without grabbing hold of the silver lining (the lesson) from the dark clouds.

I also have built a Self-Care Toolkit for myself through the years, although I wasn't consciously aware I was building up an arsenal of tools at the time. Through the Pandemic lockdowns, when I was in my self-reflection mode, I realized that I had built up quite an armament, and I will present these to you in Section VII.

I have shared with you some of the harsh and 'sucky' realities of what I have experienced as a woman through the aging process, but aging is not all doom and gloom, not by a long shot.

Are you ready for the good stuff? In the next section, I will share with you some of the glorious benefits I have learned and earned.

"I love my age. I am old enough to know better but young enough not to care. I am experienced enough to do it right."

—AUTHOR UNKNOWN

"AS GOOD AS I ONCE WAS" —Toby Keith
Yup, what he says!

You're Gonna Love Aging

BACKGROUND FOR PART V:

There are extraordinary benefits (Superpowers) that you will discover as you add another candle to your cake every year. I am going to be talking about:

- Self-Love
- Regrets, Risk-Taking, and Reinvention
- Strength and Wisdom
- Divine Feminine and Divine Masculine Energies
- Intuition

Self-love was a foreign concept that I had to force myself into. It came late in the game for me. I now know it should have been *first* in the game. I hope it is a priority for you. If you learn to love yourself just as you are, it will become one of your Superpowers. Self-love and knowing your worth are critical to anyone's life. This one is H.U.G.E.

I wish I had had the self-mastery and courage to take more significant risks much earlier. I hope that you will have the courage to do so.

I also tapped into Divine Feminine (DF) and Divine Masculine (DM) energies later in my life. In the spirit of paying it forward, I would be remiss if I didn't share the power of learning how to balance your DF and DM energies. Learn about and deploy these as you see fit.

My inner strength, the knowledge I have picked up along my journey, and the wisdom of knowing how and when to follow my intuition, are the best skills I have in my arsenal.

First, I will share with you the live operational and functional benefits that I have enjoyed from aging.

Just as in Parts II and III, where I offered you ideas to help temper the physical and emotional age markers, I will continue to provide you with "Words of Wisdom" at the end of each chapter.

And just as David Bowie's song "*Changes*" helped me frame up some of the harsh and challenging realities of the physical elements of the aging process, Mr. Bowie comes through again to usher us into our next section:

> *"Aging is an extraordinary process where you become the person you always should have been."*
>
> —DAVID BOWIE

CHAPTER 30

Gonna Be a Transformation

*"The wiser mourns less for what age takes
away than what it leaves behind."*

—WILLIAM WORDSWORTH

*M*y "Why I Love Aging" list is much longer than my "Why Aging Sucks" list. Feel free to circle, highlight, or check off those you connect with and add some of your own.

GONE FROM:	TO:
Fear of failure	Taking risks
Body image issues	Take me as I am
What if it doesn't…	What if it does…
Hang on a bit longer	Cut bait
Tried and true	Try new things
Holding a grudge	Forgiveness: It's for me, not for them
Tolerance for bullsh*t from others	No fricking way
Caring what others say	Not my business
What if I fail?	What if I fly?
Reluctance	Boldness
Unsure and insecure	Confident
Loving others first	Loving myself first
Being whom others thought I should be	Being myself
I failed	I learned
Competing with other women	Supporting and cheering on other women
Working my a*s off for someone else	Goodbye Tension. Hello Pension!
Holding onto the past	Letting sh*t go
Obeying all the rules	Rules are just guidelines. I get to choose.
Sun Worshipper	Sunscreen Guru
Trying to fit in	Being completely authentic

GONE FROM:	TO:
Not showing any weakness	Being completely vulnerable
Holding myself back	Putting myself out there
Being invisible to others	Being invincible for myself
Loving parent	Loving parent + over-the-top grandparent
Playing it safe	Taking risks
Being called "miss"	Being called "ma'am"
Playing small	Living with purpose and intention
Comparing myself to others	Accepting who I am
Being hard on myself	Being my own best friend and fan
Making self-deprecating remarks about my age	1958 was a very good year
Self-blame and self-shame	Self-care and self-celebrations
Sh*t happens	Shift happened/happens
Defining myself by my career	Defining myself by my values

Why not start your list as you see it? It's never too early or too late.

All this growth didn't happen to me overnight. I'm glad it didn't. I would have missed some of the richest lessons I learned the hard way.

I also have learned to walk away from people and situations that threaten my peace of mind, self-respect, and self-worth. This is hugely self-empowering and is worthy of Superpower status. I learned this lesson much too late in life. Don't make the same mistake. Seriously. Don't.

I know where I am today and how I feel about my age, emotionally and physically. I feel as good about it and the "more-to-come" aging as I believe I can. Contentment, acceptance of it all, and what it shall be.

I will not punish you with how, why, when, and where I made all these shifts, but I will share a few. Some, if not most, have even become my Superpowers.

The span of time and occurrences along my Hero's Journey brought about most of these changes, and I did the inner work. I took notes from all my teachers at the School of Hard Knocks, who supported my transitions.

Most of these transitions came gradually, and few were one-hit wonders. Some lessons come along as *"A-ha"* moments. It's like the lighthouse effect. You finally see the light through all the fog. I'm sure you know what I mean.

"THIS ONE'S FOR THE GIRLS"—Martina McBride
This one is for all the girls of all ages!

CHAPTER 31

Self-Love is the Greatest Love of All!

The most important relationship you will ever have is the one between you and you.

t 64 years of age, I am much more self-aware than I have ever been in my entire life. I know I went through most of my life with a disconnect between who I thought I was supposed to be, who I believed I had to be for others, and who I am. Time has allowed me to garner a heightened awareness of what I brought to my situations and experiences. It is like some purification process occurred within me along the way.

For most of my life, there seemed to be a disconnect, a gap between who I really am and who others thought I should be. I feel like I have now closed that gap. Certainly, my parents had expectations about how I should behave and conduct myself, and those expectations were quite solid and framed up by my value system. But, along the way, others also put their expectations on me as to what type of friend/wife/mother/work colleague I should be. These further shaped and defined me.

I can now look back and say that I also defined myself by keeping true to my values and belief systems. Any disconnect I felt was mine alone, and nothing was imposed upon me by anyone or anything because I didn't allow myself the time to get to know myself when I was a younger woman.

After age 20, I was busy getting my university degree part-time while working full-time and raising a young family. I built my busyness as a distraction to avoid doing internal work on those squishy and secretive parts I kept deep inside.

My 30s and 40s were very fast-flowing times, and the details are a little fuzzy, not because of memory loss but because it just moved so quickly. So I ran fast in my 40s, trying to keep pace with my career and home life. I wish I had slowed down and paid more attention to myself.

I was taking care of myself physically and gaining more self-confidence, but had I asked myself, *"Do I love myself?"* I would have quickly dismissed the notion and wouldn't have even deigned to go deeper into the self-analysis.

At that time, that question would have seemed self-indulgent and selfish. My role was to love my husband, children, and family. Love *me*? What a foreign concept.

I must have been a late bloomer because it wasn't until I was 49 that I started to connect with myself on a deeper level when the Big 5-0 was looming. So I became very introspective and took stock. Fifty seemed like such a milestone, forcing me to look ahead to my future more than ever before; it became a significant pivot point.

I realized how quickly life had passed and that I was no longer walking "up the hill." I had crested, hit the summit, and would now be walking "down the hill." It hit me then that it would be a faster walk down that proverbial hill.

For those over 50, you may have reached this pivot point earlier, where you stopped, looked around, and took inventory. Or perhaps you haven't done that yet and are over age 50. That's okay. We all go through our life reviews at our own pace. But I believe that ongoing inner check-ins would have been beneficial earlier for me.

I started asking myself who I was. Was I happy with myself? Was I happy with where I was professionally and personally? What did I like about myself? What didn't I like about myself? What could I change? Should I change?

I made myself answer those questions and have since made it an ongoing practice to ask them and self-assess so I can adjust consciously and compassionately. I continue to evolve on this journey of self-discovery and self-love. It is a living thing for me and sways back and forth.

Turning 50 made me get honest with myself. At the time, I was still in a marriage that had ended years ago. I knew that how we had been living as a married couple was a clear indicator of how the rest of my life would play out if I stayed.

I faced the most significant decision of my life. I could stay put or make a critical step forward on a new path. So I became single again at 49; that was the scariest step I had ever taken.

Part of my self-love journey came about through the new forced independence that divorce brought me. I started to get to know myself more and more once I was separated. My most extensive self-growth came during my fifth decade of life. And forgive me, Charles Dickens, but:

"It was the best of times; it was the worst of times; it was the age of wisdom, it was the age of foolishness, it was the epoch of belief, it was the epoch of incredulity; it was the season of light, it was the season of darkness, it was the spring of hope, it was the winter of despair." [40]

Yes, it was all of those things. Despite my challenges, I am incredibly grateful that I dared to make this change. I learned new life skills in my 50s that resulted in my learning so much more about myself. (I will share these in Parts V-VII.) I felt as though I had liberated my true self.

And along the way, I finally came to love myself after a lot of internal work and self-reflection. I learned that I am enough, just as I am.

I also found that my self-love journey would repeatedly stop and restart because of my self-perceived body issues and the physical changes over time. My physical appearance is in its unique evolutionary state, as it is supposed to be now.

I have come to learn and accept that I am exactly where I am supposed to be. This is *my* Hero's Journey. To get to that place of self-actualization and self-love for myself, as I am right now, I had to find ways to make that happen. I own that.

> **"Love yourself the most when you feel not so lovable."**
> —MOONOMENS

I also learned that self-love isn't selfish. You can't love anyone else until you love yourself. I know my worth now. I know my uniqueness. My story is unlike anyone else's, so I take full ownership of it and am proud of it—the good, the bad and the ugly. And yes, I have all those elements in my life story. I suspect you will too.

A good friend of mine recently loaned me a book called *The Paradox of Love*, written by J. Pittman McGehee. It is a deeply profound and beautiful book. There were a number of takeaways in that book for me, but one passage stood out to me:

"We need to love and have compassion for ourselves, just as we would for any other human being. Why would we have double standards? We are loving, forgiving, accepting of others—why can we not do that for ourselves? When we talk about loving the other, we must include ourselves as being the most important significant other we could ever love."[41]

I have heard that there are only two people in your life that you need to make proud. Not your children, partner, parents, or friends.

It is your 8-year-old self and your 80-year-old self.

Isn't that powerful? Just stop and think about that for a few minutes.

What would your idealistic, inexperienced 8-year-old self think of you today?

Conversely, what would (or does) your wiser and experienced 80-year-old self think of you today?

Would they be proud of the way you've conducted yourself to date? If so, congratulations! If some things made you pause in this self-analysis, how, where, and when should you make changes? You still have time. What can you do differently? Why or why not?

Words of Wisdom: Please don't wait as long as I did to check in with yourself, and I mean, really check in with yourself. Remember, I was 49 years old when I got started. Make it an annual birthday gift for yourself. You can also do this at New Year's or perhaps seasonally or quarterly.

Take your mental and emotional temperature more often. Dive deeply into who you are and where you are and give yourself attention and self-love. Ask yourself the important questions that only you can answer. And then listen because you are your own best teacher, healer, guide, coach, and cheerleader.

Don't think of it as being self-indulgent—consider it mandatory.

I also realize that doing any personal work on yourself when you are not ready and if you feel pressured to do it can be a total waste of your time and emotional energy. So we all need to go at our own pace. And congratulate yourself for starting or even considering starting the self-assessment process.

- You set the pace.
- You set the standard.
- It is okay to ask for help.
- It is okay to ask questions.
- It is your life.
- It is worth it.
- You are worth it.
- You will be found.
- You deserve it.

"THE GREATEST LOVE OF ALL" —Whitney Houston
This song is one of the best gifts Ms. Houston gave us.
Find the greatest love of all inside of yourself.

"ME!" —Taylor Swift
(featuring Brendon Urie of Panic! At the Disco)
Did you realize you can't spell "awesome" without "me."
We'll never find another like you!

"BORN THIS WAY" —Lady Gaga
Don't take it from me… take it from Lady Gaga. There is
nothing wrong with you, just as you are. No fixing required.

CHAPTER 32

Regrets, Risk-Taking, and Reinvention

REGRETS AND RISK-TAKING:

"Regrets. I've had a few, but then again…" (You probably know how this ends.) Frank Sinatra croons about regrets in "My Way." He is right; there are some regrets you will always carry with you and some you will eventually let go of.

I have had regrets, mostly about not taking bigger chances and opportunities when they were presented to me.

One regret that will forever haunt me was when an incredible promotional career opportunity was laid out in front of me. The reasons for not taking hold of this "golden ring" were related to my family. What I will say, in hindsight, is that I should have grabbed hold of it. In my gut, I felt this one was right. My intuition was

199

screaming at me to take it. One mindset shift that has helped me is that I also have learned that sometimes life's detours come along for a reason, and there are gifts to be found on any path and with every choice.

I, of course, have experienced other regrets that were much easier to pass off, like harsh words being spoken in the heat of the moment, or words I wish I had said. Haven't we all had *"would-a, could-a, should-a"* moments?

Why do we always think of the most brilliant rebuttals after the fact? You know what I'm talking about, don't you?

But typically, those "Why did I/didn't I say that?" self-judgments don't hang around and haunt us. It's the regrets that could have positively changed our life trajectories that do. So, be bold. But be smart. Trust your intuition—it is your guiding light.

Many of us are overthinkers. We try to project, estimate, research, and calculate all the potential "what-ifs" of an opportunity, situation, or conversation. Of course, it is helpful to be prepared and informed, but I have discovered that overthinking can also be paralyzing. We feed ourselves TMI, don't we?

Now I realize that you must be brave enough to take the first step into something that can be scary. Trust yourself. Take the chance. Take the risk. I only regretted the opportunities I didn't take.

I have a sign on my Vision Board that reads *"No Regrets!"* as a constant reminder to be bolder and take more chances. At 64, I can almost hear that sign ticking at me. I know it is much easier and less frightening to play it safe, so I need the visual nudge.

Me authoring this book and putting myself out there in the world in this manner would once have been unthinkable. I had an epiphany during the Pandemic, however. Should we ever come out of lockdown, I would:

*"Take more risks, have no regrets, live
larger, live louder, and have fun."*

So, I am taking this risk. *Yee-haw!!* I know I will have critics. I have dealt with critics my entire life (and you may have too), but at this stage, I no longer spend much time thinking about them or giving them any of my energy.

*"Twenty years from now, you will be more disappointed
by the things you didn't do than by the ones you did.
So, throw off the bowlines.
Sail away from the safe harbour.
Catch the trade winds in your sails.
Explore. Dream. Discover."*

—SARAH FRANCIS BROWN
(often believed to be from Mark Twain)

Words of Wisdom: Reduce your regrets. Take a risk by leaping into the unknown. It will be scary sometimes. Stretch yourself, make yourself uncomfortable; you're growing. Don't put yourself in a position where you will regret that you didn't take the risk. Please don't have any more *"would-a, should-a, could-a's"* in your life. Take it from me; these can be hard to shake off.

REINVENTION:

Through the Pandemic, I also plugged into Arlene Dickinson's *"Reinvention"* podcast while escaping outside on my socially-distanced walks. I was mesmerized by the interviews she held with many wonderful and successful people (many of them Canadian). Hearing their stories made me look inwardly at myself and consider how many reinventions I have had to go through in my lifetime.

Here's a quick-hit list:

- I have gone from being single to being married.
- I returned to school part-time while working full-time.
- I have had two pregnancies and two children.
- I got divorced and am single again.
- I dated again. And again.
- I became a grandmother.
- I retired.
- I became an author (*The word "author" still startles me.*)

In addition, I had fourteen distinct roles in my professional corporate life in thirty-seven years (with the same company), and I worked in several law offices before that! Baby, I have been working a long time! That is a lot of change to assimilate.

I recall being so excited, but scared and way out of my depth, in a few of those positions. I can tell you my knees were trembling under those L'eggs™ pantyhose *(remember those?)* on more than one occasion throughout my career.

I'm competitive by nature, so I knew that when those scary—yet—exciting opportunities were presented to me, I had to prove to the doubters (and there were many) and to *myself* that I could rise to the challenge. It was my chance to sink or swim.

The challenge, the fear, the doubts, and the excitement drove me.

If you have ever been there, you know you have to grab hold and give it the best you have. Stretch yourself into it. Despite my fears and self-doubts, I figured it all out—every single time. I swam, baby. I'll bet you do, too. As Dori from *Finding Nemo* says: *"Just keep swimming, just keep swimming."*

All my personal and professional reinventions required me to adjust to accommodate and assimilate them into my life. Most women will have these or remarkably similar circumstances and changes. I am not unique here.

Or you could have had quite different circumstances that you have been living through. The key is for you to stop and think about your own life and consider all the reinventions you have already gone through. Don't forget about your WW#, you Wonder Woman, you!

> *"All of us will face moments of insecurity and doubt—moments where we feel unworthy. Know that these moments are often nothing more than self-imposed limitations. So get out there and do your best. You will refine, grow, and enhance your ideas when you let them flow out to a world that will dissect, comment on, engage with, and mould them. Let public opinion and feedback become your friends. No matter where you are, put your insecurities aside and just do it."*
>
> —VISHEN LAKHIANI

Even at age 64, I have reinvented myself since becoming a retiree. Indeed the Pandemic played a role, as we were all put through a forced reinvention, reset, and reboot.

I am comfortable with reinventing myself because I know how to do it. I've done it many times before, so I am confident that I can continue to reimagine, readjust, and reinvent my life as I need to or want to. I want to keep evolving and pushing myself forward with new adventures.

Jann Arden sees it this way: *"What I think about now couldn't be further from brooding on time running out. Instead, I'm focused on reimagining and reinvention, the act of becoming someone I always hoped I would be. I feel that I am a wise woman emerging through the trees with a renewed sense of purpose in my own glorious life."*[42]

Yes! Exactly how I feel! Thank you. Ms. Arden, you continue to rock our worlds in more ways than one, and I am of course, also referring to your brilliant musical career.

Words of Wisdom: If you need to step outside yourself to get some inspiration to help you find a new path forward, I invite you to connect to Arlene Dickinson's "Reinvention" podcast series. (See Appendix B.)

Listen to these amazing stories. These phenomenally successful people share how they learned, grew, and moved on from their setbacks. I was magnetized to this podcast and always felt so inspired by her guests. I suspect you will feel not only inspired, but also encouraged. Make it happen. Be the Phoenix.

Words of Wisdom: Think about reinvention as it relates to your life. How many times have you had to reinvent yourself already? Think about the strength and courage it must have taken for you to make those changes. Journal about it. I suspect it is far more than you initially thought.

To anyone who has found themselves, willingly or unwillingly, in a position where they need to "reinvent" themselves, I say:

Setbacks pave the way for comebacks. I hope you have a fantastic comeback.

"Be the Phoenix

If you can honour the story that got you to today,
If you can honour the strength you showed in keeping to the trail,
If you can pay homage to the tragedies that revealed how deep and truly loving you are,
If you can look back and see the beauty of your soul growing,
Through all the difficult moments when it felt like you were locked in an invisible prison
A beautiful life you will feel around you now.
The sacredness of your breath.
The fact that you have so much behind you because you kept going.
Tell your story without hanging your head in shame.
Tell your story with your head held high because you became the hero you needed.
You got yourself to today.
For that alone, you should be really proud."

—CHERYL ALLEN

"MY WAY" —Frank Sinatra
As Frankie Blue-Eyes croons, do it your way. Have no regrets.

"LOSE YOURSELF" —Eminem
This song always rocks my world. It will force you to shoot your
shot; when you get that one shot, just take it! *Alexa: Repeat!*

"TAKIN' CARE OF BUSINESS" —Bachman-Turner Overdrive
Rock out to BTO when you need some to feel uplifted.

By the way, Randy Bachman was one of Arlene Dickinson's
"Reinvention" podcast guests. Check it out on Episode 12.
He shares a remarkable story. Two great Canadians!

"GOOD MOTHER" —Jann Arden
A remarkable Canadian artist who beautifully tells
us to stay grounded, and *"just be yourself."*

CHAPTER 33

Strength and Wisdom

y strength, resilience, and wisdom grew from all the changes and challenges I encountered along my life's path. Some changes I initiated; many were "gifted" to me. I have learned that things don't happen to you. They happen for you. They are karmic lessons and cycles.

Some of those lessons were brutally hard, and I remember thinking I would never get through them, but I did. Moreover, I learned so much about myself and others that I labelled those lessons *"silver linings."* Bear in mind that while I lived through them, there was nothing illustrious like silver about them. Absolutely not.

At times, my emotions, pride, self-confidence, and self-esteem were in tatters. I was trying to hold my sh*t together and find a way forward. And like the Bee Gees sing, I was simply "Stayin' Alive."

But enough of the drama. What is important is that I got through "it" every time. Maybe a little bruised up, but sooooo much wiser. So let me share a few pearls of wisdom I have learned through the years.

- Karma is a b*tch—I have met her.
- I have watched that b*tch bite others as well, but Karma doesn't always work as fast as I think she should.

"Life Isn't Fair.

"No matter what life throws your way, no matter how unfair it may seem, refuse to play the victim. Refuse to be ruled by fear, pessimism, and negativity. Refuse to quit.

"Be a warrior and work through whatever life throws your way with courage, love, and positivity. And continually push forward.

"Because you are a survivor of the unfairness of life. You are stronger than you think. And you are capable of achieving far more than you believe."

—ZERO DEAN

I would have loved that quote when I was much younger, so I could have seared it into my soul and belief system.

I built my strength, grit, and resilience during the harshest lessons. I got through my challenging times by journalling, doing much internal soul-searching, and purging all the dark shadows lurking around.

I learned to deploy gratitude practices in a much more significant way than just saying "thank you."

I learned about the healing power of forgiveness.

I learned how to release the past.

And I healed with music.

The best lessons often hurt the most. First, you must walk through the thorns to get to the roses. Just like Poison sings: "Every Rose Has Its Thorn." I learned that you can't circumvent the pain, nor can you bury it and think that's the end of it.

You have to deal with it head-on, hands on and heart open.

Every lesson helped me learn more about who I am and, in turn, deepened my wisdom.

"Wisdom is knowing when to use what you learned to make a situation in your life better. Your wisdom becomes one of your most trusted sources for guidance."
—AUTHOR UNKNOWN

And I found my way forward. Time and self-reflection were the best antidotes to recover and learn from my most challenging lessons.

My good, bad, and ugly adventures have shaped me and taught me so much. I have made some big mistakes. I still do. But I no longer beat myself up about them. I now do my best to give myself grace, accept them, and, most importantly, grow from them.

*"I have learned so much from my mistakes
that I must make a few more."*

There really is a silver lining in every cloud. So cliché, but so frigging true. Sometimes you need to dig and claw through a lot of grey to find it, but I promise you, it is there.

This may sound very warped, but I have been blessed to have gone through a few walks through the thorns. There are always roses on the other side. The learnings and the lessons are worth the pain. However I would have never said that while walking through the thorns.

Words of Wisdom: It doesn't matter what life situation occurs; you should always do a post-mortem on it and look for the silver lining. If you choose to do this, you will always come away with something—more insight, wisdom, power, courage, and clarity. Be sure to allow yourself the time and space to heal and recover from any challenging life experience.

"Turn your wounds into wisdom."
—OPRAH WINFREY

Words of Wisdom: Make a conscious decision to transmute all the pain you're feeling into power. Reframe it. When you're ready emotionally, physically, and mentally, do a purge. Don't bury it inside (pain, hurt, anger, jealousy, shame, betrayal, fear, revenge, etc.). It doesn't go away; it resurfaces until you release it. You deserve the peace of mind.

"STAYIN' ALIVE" —Bee Gees
This song is all about perseverance and survival, and determination. Strong message, with a kick-ass beat!

"EVERY ROSE HAS ITS THORN" —Poison
I love this song, and its title fits in with my earlier analogy. You're welcome.

"I WILL SURVIVE" —Gloria Gaynor
The song's message is all about perseverance and resilience.
It is considered an anthem of female empowerment.

CHAPTER 34

How Divine

"Your energy introduces you before you even speak."
—MEL ROBBINS

W ithin the past few years, I have become familiar with Divine Feminine (DF) and Divine Masculine (DM) energies. I don't know why I hadn't found out about this earlier, but I believe everything comes to you when it is supposed to.

This information would have been invaluable to me as a young woman and throughout my entire life. I wish I had it in my Self-Care Toolkit as a teenager. Not sure I would have been mature enough to discriminate on when to use these energies then, but certainly, I could have used a deeper knowledge throughout my career and in my adult relationships.

In my working days, I was deploying these energies to some extent, but I definitely could have used some coaching and refinement. So, I have decided to provide you with a crash course and preliminary understanding if you don't know about these energies yet.

DF and DM do not relate to female and male physical characteristics. These are also not related to gender expression. Instead, DF and DM relate to our spiritual energies, our presence, how we feel connected to ourselves and how we project to the world.

Both women and men have DF and DM energies at our disposal. It is up to us to tap into and direct these energies. They can be natural and inherent, but you can also learn how to strengthen them. Most of us have a tendency to lean more toward one or the other, which may not have any correlation to our physical gender. You can learn how and when to embody your DF and DM energies based on different situations.

At a very basic level, here are the differences between DF and DM energies:

> *"While definitions will vary among spiritualists, the Divine Feminine is generally thought to represent the part of our consciousness that connects us to qualities like intuition, feeling, nurturing, receptivity, and interconnectedness. It's a type of energy everyone can access and tap into—not something tangible, not a secret club that you need a membership to access."*
>
> —NINA KHAN

"The Divine Feminine refers to the face of the divine spirit connected with the body, nature, and the cycles of creation and transformation. It is generally understood and felt through the subtle intuitive wisdom of the body. You can think of tapping into DF energy as embracing your inner Goddess."

—GABRIELA HERSTICK

Conversely, Elana Kilkenny, who is an Intuitive Counsellor, defines Divine Masculine as:

"It's all about structure, logic, and taking charge. Divine Masculine energy is at play with things like assertiveness, confidence, speaking up for yourself, and sometimes, fighting the good fight.

"Where Divine Feminine energy can be more passive and willing to compromise, sometimes there are things in the world we need to fight for and situations where we need to draw a line about what's right or wrong. Our Divine Masculine energy is good at setting boundaries in this way.

"Similarly, this plays into the idea of strength, not just physical but emotional strength. Divine Masculine energy is deeply connected to the warrior within each of us.

"Where Divine Feminine energy can be very internal and reflective, Divine Masculine energy relishes doing things in the real world, like having adventures, making changes, saying what's on your mind, and taking risks. It's also an energy that's often associated with things like logic and critical thinking."

It's important to know how and when to dial in and connect with your DF and DM. Different scenarios call for different energies.

My career was founded in the late '70s when very few women were in leadership roles. But the woman's movement had been stirred again with the release of "I Am Woman" (Helen Reddy) in 1972. Her song has even been called a "cultural touchstone" for the times. This song is beautifully woven between DF and DM but heavy on the DM.

And women were singing it and stepping up to prove their equality with men. Do you recall when further momentum was added to the movement by the defeat of Bobby Riggs by Billie Jean King in their *"Battle of the Sexes"* tennis match in 1973?

So when I got my first real job in the '70s, women were leaning into their DM energies in the workforce to be taken seriously, but by the early '80s, it was equally important for women to present themselves as DF.

Like Steve Harvey coaches: "Women had to think like men but act like ladies." [43] *(Yes, I know Mr. Harvey's advice refers to the mating and dating game, and that his book wasn't even written until 2009, but it fits here, too. Thank you, Mr. Harvey.)*

It was a time when women were being encouraged, by other women, to have it all.

Recall that jingle from the Enjoli™ perfume commercial from the '80s:

> "I can bring home the bacon.
>
> Fry it up in a pan.
>
> And never, never let him forget he's the man!
>
> 'Cause I'm a woman!"

If you were a woman in the workforce during the '80s, I can almost guarantee that you will still recall this jingle. You can sing along, am I right? I certainly can, and in my mind's eye, I can still see the actress from that commercial. She was pretty fricking inspiring to me.

That commercial probably wouldn't fly today, but as women, we were busting our butts to have it all back then. We were self-empowering ourselves. Despite what we might think of that commercial today, it's an excellent example of how women sought to balance their DF essence while busting out their DM attitudes back in the '80s.

Since becoming more aware and educated on Divine Femininity and Divine Masculinity, I have learned how to consciously identify which energy I am in and how to adjust my DF or DM energies when circumstances dictate. In hindsight, I recognize I was already doing this, even early in my career, but believe me, I was not proficient. It takes practice and confidence to strike the balance you need for different situations.

Words of Wisdom: A ton of information is available if you want to learn more about DF and DM energies. I promise you that these DF and DM energies you can learn to activate and embody will serve you well throughout your Life's Trimesters. I wish I had known about these energies earlier. This is powerful stuff.

Words of Wisdom: Tony Robbins offers a free online quiz on his website to identify if your DF or DM energies are most prevalent. Don't shortchange yourself on this free five-minute quiz. It might reveal or confirm your gut feelings. *P.S. That's your DF showing.* (See the QR Code link in Appendix B.) Thank you, Mr. Robbins.

Words of Wisdom: Don't be reluctant to imbue and flow with your DF essence, yet be sure to flex your Divine Masculinity, as only you can determine. *Vive la différence!*

Here are a few song choices to tap into your DF and DM energies. Try these out during any *Mirror, Mirror* work. (See Chapter 39.)

"I AM WOMAN" —Helen Reddy
Straight from the '70s archives. Ms. Reddy belts this out in her classic Divine Masculine energy while standing up in her Divine Feminine power. This song broke new ground when it was released and became symbolic of the feminist movement.

"LOVER" —Taylor Swift
DF and DM. Ms. Swift nails this one. In my
opinion, this is a perfect balance between DF
and DM. Brilliant! Thank you, Ms. Swift.

"I PUT A SPELL ON YOU" —Creedence Clearwater Revival
Girl, this is one you want to dirty dance to, with a partner or
not. It will get you all up in your dark DF side. You're welcome.

"CONFIDENT" —Demi Lovato
Ms. Lovato has got this all figured out. Listen
and learn. It's a masterclass in DF and DM.

"UNSTOPPABLE" —Sia
This is DM all the way. Put your armour on.
You are stronger than you realize. This song
has female warrior vibes. Be invincible.

CHAPTER 35

Intuition

*I*ntuition is defined as:

"1a: the power or faculty of attaining direct knowledge or cognition without evident rational thought and inference

1b: immediate apprehension or cognition

2: quick and ready insight"[44]

—Merriam-Webster Dictionary

Intuition is your spidey sense, that niggling feeling, that internal nudge, that *"Je ne c'est quoi"* type of feeling. It comes from your most authentic self. It is every woman's inherent Superpower. Baby, you were born with it.

I always have discovered that if something doesn't feel right, it isn't. I have come to trust that feeling. Respectfully, so should you.

I have done a tremendous amount of business travel on my own through the years. I have had several uncomfortable situations that I extricated myself from because I sensed something was off.

Once, while travelling alone on a business trip to Vancouver, I had flown in the late afternoon, and given the three-hour time difference, I was more than ready for dinner. I checked into my hotel room and went to the hotel dining room for dinner. I stopped in their gift shop across from the restaurant to buy a magazine to enjoy with my dinner. While there, I noticed a man, but we didn't exchange greetings.

So I was surprised while I was in the restaurant waiting to be seated when this gentleman came up quietly behind me and said to the hostess, *"Could you seat us together for dinner?"*

I turned and said, *"Oh no, thank you, I would prefer to have dinner on my own."*

He tried to coax me into it, but I was polite and said, *"No, I am looking forward to relaxing and reading my magazine over dinner."* The hostess started to lead me into the restaurant, and I asked her to ensure that she sat the gentleman some distance away from me. She understood immediately, sat me down, and then seated him across the restaurant from me.

So much for my relaxing dinner… I was quick to get through my meal and didn't linger. I paid my cheque and was on my way back to my room. I thought that was the end of it.

While returning to my room, I walked down a hallway with a large window at the end, and I could see my reflection in it. I was taken aback by this man scurrying behind to catch up to me. Yikes!

I picked up my pace and got to the front desk. I told them that I was being followed and to please not draw any attention to it. I pretended I was having a conversation with the front desk staff about something.

Sure enough, the man passed by and lingered around the elevators. I stayed put, pretending I was still conversing with staff and letting their hotel security handle it. The hotel security guard started walking toward the elevators—the man quickly got into the elevator, and thankfully, that was the last I saw of him. The security guard came back and escorted me to my room afterwards. All ended well, and I was grateful to have the support from the hotel staff.

But I immediately knew something was off when I turned around in that restaurant. I didn't feel compelled to be polite and have dinner with him or speak with him in any way. I didn't question my feeling. I trusted it... I knew this was not a good individual to engage with.

Trust that little niggly feeling inside of you. It can be subtle or scream at you. The sooner you take action, the better. Act when you first sense, hear, or feel those internal whispers. Don't wait for your intuition to yell at you, and don't worry about what anyone else thinks.

Do what you need to do to extricate yourself from the person, place, thing, or situation. Be smart. Be safe. Don't ever compromise yourself here.

Of course, intuition doesn't just come in handy only for safety's sake.

You're also tuned into intuition when you have a great idea or a "Eureka!" moment. You just know when all the pieces fit and finally come together. Right?

When was your last "gut feel" about someone or something? Do you act on it? Or did you ignore it? How did that work out for you? I sincerely hope it ended well for you.

Your "gut feel" covers both spectrums, from the best to the worst. Use your body as an energy source. Trust your own instincts.

Words of Wisdom: Are you aware of the *"The Violence at Home Signal for Help*™?

The Canadian Women's Foundation brilliantly created a "Signal for Help"[45] during the Pandemic as a way to signal on a video call that you need help from a domestic abuse situation.

While women, girls, and gender-diverse people are more at risk of gender-based violence, the Signal for Help was created for anyone to use, not just women working from home during the Pandemic.

I urge you to become familiar with it—for yourself, your family, and your friends. Be aware if you see anyone using it and find a way to help. (Check out the link in Appendix B.)

Words of Wisdom: If you need help tapping into your intuition, I came across a phenomenal coach called Sonia Choquette. I encourage you to listen to her on YouTube.™ *"How to Tune Into and Trust Your Intuition."* (See link in Appendix B.)

"INTUITION" —Jewel
Just follow your heart, baby!

CHAPTER 36

Be Brave!

PART V SUMMARY

How are you feeling now after reading this section? Optimistic? Doubtful? Fearful? Or are you going to go all Valley Girl on me, say, "*Whatever!*" flip your hair back, and carry on?

- I hope you feel inspired and empowered.
- It takes courage to do some deep dives on yourself and peel back the layers.
- It also takes courage to admit your mistakes and learn from your mistakes.

- The benefits of getting older are spectacular. Who knew? Now you know!
- You are gonna love it!
- Soak it in and revel in it!
- Celebrate it—you're only getting better, baby!
- It just keeps getting better and better. Seriously.
- Do something that scares you. Then do something else that scares you. You will grow so much from the risk, the challenge, and the lessons.

"BRAVE" —Sara Bareilles
Show up for yourself and show the world how big your brave is. Of course, we all get scared. So have Alexa put this on "repeat" when you need to get your brave on. A powerful song for all of us!

Your Self-Care Toolkit

BACKGROUND FOR PART VI:

I did so many things the hard way because, at the time, I didn't know any better. So I am sharing some of these tools I have discovered in Parts VI and VII. Most women 40 or 50+ have built toolkits of their own, but we can always add more to our kits, inspire one another, and find new ways or greater motivation to use the tools we already have.

If you are still in your 1st or even 2nd Trimester of Life, some of my lessons will resonate, and some won't—yet. I am giving you a heads-up. I wish I had had more of these tools in my hot little hands in my 1st and 2nd Trimesters.

Toolkit:
I found that I needed to build tools to help navigate the aging or "growing up" process.

I imagine how these tools might have changed the trajectory of my life had I had them years or decades earlier. I would have loved more self-confidence and self-awareness when I was younger.

I am grateful that I have this toolkit now! I can pick up the right tools whenever I need them. And I am happy to share these with you.

At the end of each chapter, I continue to serve up my unsolicited *"Words of Wisdom."* It's that, *"I know you're not asking, but if you were, here's what I would offer"* approach. Please take it or leave it. You do you.

Sometimes the hardest thing to do is admit you need help. I have learned that it is okay and even recommended to receive support when needed, and there shouldn't be any shame in that. Women tend to be over-givers, so please allow yourself to receive. Once we surrender to the ask, the Universe will find ways to deliver it. *(Now that was "woo-woo!")*

CHAPTER 37

Your Self-Care Toolkit

Affirmations

*W*hile going through the most extensive self-discovery phase in my 50s, I found that I needed to give myself a boost to get my self-love party started.

As I mentioned, self-love didn't come easily to me. I needed to encourage myself along the way by writing affirmations to guide me. Do you know what I mean by "affirmations?" I am referring to the *"I am..."* positive statements.

Here's some more *"woo-woo"* for you, all dressed up in a very corny analogy I heard somewhere and cannot remember where, but it seems like a nod back to my country roots, so I'm sharing it:

- I have learned that writing and reciting positive affirmations is akin to planting my annual flower seedlings in my garden. When I plant those seedlings in my garden in the spring, I know they need time to sprout and fully take root; stems and leaves will shoot out of the ground towards the sunlight, and eventually, my flowers will bloom.

- I trust that my flowers will grow and bloom so long as I continue to water and care for them. This is the same for my positive affirmations. I know they need time to take hold within me, and like my flower seedlings, my affirmations also will bloom and manifest into my reality because my mind soaks in what I feed it.

Initially, it felt so awkward and self-indulgent when I started to say my affirmations out loud. But with practice, it became more comfortable and started to feel more genuine. I post them on my bulletin board in my home office so they are a visual reminder for me to recite them. Even just silently reading them likely does some good, but they are even more powerful when we say them aloud, with feeling. My affirmations form part of my Self-Care Toolkit.

Writing out and declaring my affirmations is a dynamic, not a static process. After using some for a while, I will feel an inner, *"Yes of course, that's true! I don't need to keep saying it anymore."* This is a good sign because I have integrated it as my inner truth. We are all always evolving, so expect to graduate to new affirmations as you heal, grow, and deepen your self-love and self-care.

Words of Wisdom: We will all face moments of self-doubt, and our insecurities will challenge our self-worth. I have learned to take a leap of faith many times and set my insecurities aside. I can also tell you that it can be challenging to do. Writing out *"I am"* affirmations has been a good practice for me that's helped me overcome self-doubts.

I have listed some sample affirmations below (from lifehack.org), which you can use to get started. I understand, however, that affirmations should be relevant and unique to a person's needs, so write your own if these don't resonate.

Just be sure to keep them positive. "I don't want to feel so stressed" is not going to work, whereas "I stay calm and focused" or "I am peaceful and positive" pack a good positivity punch.

Then say them out loud. Fight through any awkwardness as you do so. I had to. It may feel forced at first. When I started this practice, I felt so phoney, but there's a "fake it until you make it" here.

Writing out the *"I am"* affirmations can get you into the zone. Post them and say them aloud daily until you believe them and *feel* them. Additionally, looking at yourself in the mirror while you recite them strengthens the affirmations. Make it a part of your *Mirror, Mirror* technique as well. Seriously. (See Chapter 39.)

My daughter even has taught her children, under five years of age, to recite age-appropriate *"I am"* affirmations. What an excellent practice to build her children's self-esteem and self-worth early on. Reciting affirmations is a best practice for anyone at any age.

Feel free to access this *"I am..."* listing on my website at www. Brenda.Ackerman.com if you wish to print this listing.

"Think of this as a menu of options. Each morning, select a few, say them out loud, write them down, or say them all! Doing this will set the tone for your day and get you moving positively:

1. I am confident.
2. I am powerful.
3. I am strong.
4. I am getting better and better every day.
5. All I need is within me right now.
6. I wake up motivated.
7. I am an unstoppable force of nature.
8. I am a living, breathing example of motivation.
9. I am living with abundance.
10. I am having a positive and inspiring impact on the people I come into contact with.
11. I am inspiring people through my work.
12. Today is a phenomenal day.
13. I am turning DOWN the volume of negativity while simultaneously turning UP the volume of positivity.
14. I am focused.
15. My problems do not push me; my dreams lead me.
16. I am grateful for everything I have.
17. I am independent and self-sufficient.
18. I can be whatever I want to be.
19. My past does not define me; my future drives me
20. I use obstacles to motivate me to learn and grow.
21. Today will be a productive day.
22. I am intelligent and focused.
23. I feel more grateful each day.

24. I am getting healthier every day.

25. Every day, I am getting closer to achieving my goals.

26. Through the power of my thoughts and words, incredible transformations are happening in me and within my life.

27. I am constantly growing and evolving into a better person.

28. I accept myself for who I am and create peace, power, and confidence of mind and heart.

29. I forgive myself and free myself, and I deserve to forgive and be forgiven.

30. I am healing and strengthening every day.

31. I've made it through hard times before, and I've become stronger and better because of them. So I'm going to make it through this.

32. I do not waste away a single day of my life. Instead, I squeeze every ounce of value out of my days on this planet—today, tomorrow, and every day.

33. I must remember the incredible power I possess to achieve anything I desire.

34. I do not engage with people who try to penetrate my mind with unhelpful thoughts and ideas—I walk away when a person or a situation isn't healthy for me.

35. I belong in this world; some people care about me and my worth.

36. I am beautiful.

37. I have made mistakes but will not let them define me.

38. My soul radiates from the inside and warms the souls of others.

39. I don't compare myself to others. The only person I compare myself to is the person I was yesterday. And as long as the person I am today is even the tiniest bit better than the person I was yesterday—I'm meeting my definition of success.

40. Note to self: I will make you proud.
41. I finish what matters and let go of what does not.
42. I feed my spirit and train my body. I focus my mind. This is my time.
43. My life has meaning, what I do has meaning, and my actions are meaningful and inspiring.
44. What I did today was the best I could do today. And for that, I am thankful.
45. One small positive thought in the morning can change my day. So, today I rise with a powerful thought to set the tone and allow success to reverberate through every moment of my day.
46. I set goals and go after them with all the determination I can muster. When I do this, my skills and talents will take me to places that amaze me.
47. Happiness is a choice; today, I choose to be happy." [46]

"I AM…I SAID" —Neil Diamond
I'll bet any 5th grader could figure out why I chose this song.

"I AM WOMAN" —Emmy Meli
This song is about living in your total Divine
Feminine and Divine Masculine. Please don't
sleep on this one—play it repeatedly until you get
it goin' on. Ms. Meli will show you the way.

CHAPTER 38

Your Self-Care Toolkit

Journalling

ne of the greatest tools I have in my Self-Care Kit is journalling.

I hadn't kept a diary since I was 10 years old, so how odd that I would resume the practice 40 years later. I don't address my notes with *"Dear Diary"* like I did when I was 10 though.

I honestly don't remember how I started journalling again. I remember that I would sometimes get on my computer, open a Word™ document, and start pounding on the keys when I was pissed off to let off some steam. Then, somehow along the way, I gravitated to a journal and pen, which has become my go-to practice. Writing my thoughts in my journal has become my favourite tool in my Self-Care Toolkit.

What a wonderful cathartic practice journalling is! I cannot recommend it highly enough to anyone, no matter the stage of their life. I even see my young grandchildren, who are just learning how to print, take out paper and draw out their thoughts and stories, and I had forgotten how it comes so naturally at an incredibly early age.

I wish I had kept a diary since I was 10 years old; it would have been so helpful through the past 50+ years of my life to write out my thoughts and deal with them through this cleansing release of pen on paper.

I have lost count of the number of journals I have written since I turned 50. I always handwrite them. I find my musings highly influenced by a glass or two of a lovely Pinot Grigio, when all my inhibitions have been relaxed. (Although it's totally fine to journal without alcohol.) And most certainly, I always get into a journalling frame of mind by turning on some music. *Et voila*, it just all comes pouring out—both the wine and my thoughts! So I let my mood dictate my music choices.

The songs stir up memories and emotions and put me into a frame of mind that is completely unplugged. No inhibitions, no fears, no worries—I surrender to the thoughts that percolate. I follow them, and I scribe them. This is my form of meditation.

I have never been able to be a successful meditator in the traditional "sitting still, eyes closed" sense, despite the meditation classes I have attended, so I find my journal writing takes me there and provides me with clarity, focus, peace, and direction.

My thoughts, dreams, ideas, plans, goals, fears, and hopes have been penned into my journals. I discovered that part of my self-love journey was allowing myself to feel big emotions—fear, joy, forgiveness of myself and others, anger, grace, and healing from past traumas. I had to go deep within myself as I had buried many of my feelings and emotions. Through journalling, I could work my way through and unpack a lot of emotional baggage.

It's not all love and light. I have told people to f*ck off through my written rantings. It gives me the freedom to say things I would (or could) never say in person, which lightens my emotional load. I have forgiven people through my journalling, after I had previously told these same people to f*ck off in the same journal. *Mind-blowing moments!* And most important of all, I have forgiven myself through my penned words.

I also have drawn and designed beautiful gowns and dresses in my journals. I even have designed and decorated my home through journal drawings, in between pouring my heart out and letting it bleed spilled ink onto the pages.

I have doodled and written all my secrets and truths in those beautifully bound books. And I have manifested my life goals and aspirations through those pages.

I reread them through the Pandemic, and I thought, "*OMG! If I were to die tomorrow, and should anyone, including my children, read them, they would think I was a crazed and depraved lunatic who had been on her own for far too long,*" which, I admit, could be true.

So I did what any crazed and depraved lunatic would do. I turned on my music, poured myself some wine and read through them again. It was quite a walk down memory lane, and I congratulated myself on how far I had come and assessed where I needed to do some more internal work. Then, I ripped out the pages and shredded them. But I kept my "life goals and aspirations" listings intact!

I didn't invent the concept of journalling, but I am underscoring its powers as a brilliant release and self-healing modality. I think this should be mandatory, as I suspect we would all be mentally stronger. I also have found it a fantastic way to connect with myself. Although I can type extremely fast, I choose to handwrite my entries, as it forces me to slow down, focus my thinking mentally, and go deeper inside myself.

I may be criticized because I choose to handwrite my journals rather than type them via my phone, tablet, or computer. That's most likely my age showing, and I don't care. When I don't have my journals with me and a noteworthy thought crosses my mind, I take advantage of my phone or tablet. Like Billie Eilish would say, *"D'uh!"*

You can journal any way you like but take my word for it: Do it.

And please don't get in your own way by thinking you need to be a great writer. This is not 9th-grade English class. No one will see your words but you unless you want to share them with someone. And, who knows, maybe you will discover or revive a talent for the written word. In any case, journal for YOU.

Words of Wisdom: Get a journal and start writing down your thoughts about anything and everything you want. Or get busy on your phone, computer or tablet. If you write with an app that all your devices can access, you can see what you wrote, no matter your device. Capture your thoughts when you're angry, sad, happy, disappointed, jealous, envious, curious, furious, excited, grateful, or whenever you need to unload feelings about something or someone.

It is so revealing, so cathartic, and so healing. Use your journals to design and create whatever you want. Just doodling alone can feel liberating or lead to new ideas.

I recommend that you date your entries, as it becomes an interesting walk down memory lane when you read your journals later.

Your journal should be private because it is you in your most authentic and vulnerable state. It is you—unplugged.

And if you need a few music suggestions to get you into that journalling frame of mind, here are some of my favourites:

"PURPLE RAIN" —Prince
I set the stage: lights out, candles burning,
enjoy a glass of wine, and then I queue up
Prince to serenade me with Purple Rain.

"PUT YOUR RECORDS ON" —Corinne Bailey Rae
There is just something about this song that
puts me in a carefree and open-minded mood.
Just go-with-it kind of vibe. Love it.

"MY CHURCH" —Maren Morris
A nod back to my country roots. Take the lead from
Ms. Morris and find your soul's revival by playing your
all-time favourite song to set your soul on fire.
"Can I get a "Hallelujah?"

"UNWRITTEN" —Natasha Bedingfield
Listen to her lyrics to get you into that releasing-your-inhibitions kind of zone. Write it out. Tell
your story. Today is where *your* book begins.

"BAD GUY" —Billie Eilish
Play this one when you want to bring out your "bad girl"
energies 'cause they're so good. You know you want to.

CHAPTER 39

Your Self-Care Toolkit

"Mirror, Mirror" Technique

*T*his technique is the scariest and most frightening tool in my Self-Care Toolkit, but it's one of the best for anyone struggling with their body image, or certain parts of their body, in any way.

I did not invent this technique; it has been around for years. I don't even remember where I heard about this. This exercise took me far beyond my comfort zone.

You may already be wonderfully comfortable and proficient with this activity, and I sincerely applaud you for that. We are all striving for greater self-confidence and self-acceptance on our self-love journeys.

I was, however, a reluctant participant, taking the term "slow learner" to new heights as I built up to the "Full Monty." That should be a massive clue about where I am going with this little gem.

If you need help with any part of the physiological parts of the aging process, then I especially suggest you try this exercise. I will forewarn you, though, it's not one of those "one-and-done" activities. But I promise, it *does* get easier and more powerful the more you practice it.

I do this anytime when I don't feel so good about my physical appearance and the resulting impact the WW# has had on me through the years. This exercise helps you appreciate and love your body just as it is.

For many of us, this can be incredibly challenging. I had to force myself to stick with this drill (yes, it at times felt that way). It can be brutal, raw, and revealing (pun intended), so I always need to play music to support myself mentally and emotionally.

Here is the *"Mirror, Mirror"* technique: (Be brave, my little buckaroo.)

- Your job is to lock yourself away in a room with a full-length mirror, a music source (or your phone with a QR code reader to play the music below) and get naked to look at yourself head to toe. Yikes, right?
- Start playing the music of your choice. Selecting your music selection helps to set up your frame of mind. How do you

want to feel? Brave? Confident? Powerful? Playful? Sultry? Seductive? Goddessy? Kick-assy?

- Let the music wash over you and put you in the "vibe" of how you want to feel.
- We are all our own worst critics, so talk to yourself and your body, tell yourself how beautiful you are, and appreciate your body for what it has gone through so far in life. Give yourself complete compassion.
- Don't do a tiny cursory glance; do a long, slow, appraising, and non-judgmental look. Be neutral and accepting; don't look for flaws. Look for the good.

Accept what you see exactly as you are. Exactly how Emma Thompson did it in *Good Luck to You, Leo Grande*. Thank you to the beautiful Ms. Thompson.

If naked is a non-starter for you, wear some lingerie or a bathing suit, or even stay entirely clothed until you are ready to graduate to the *"shake what your mama gave you"* level. The intention is to get truly comfortable with your body just as it is. Go at your own pace.

If you need to be even more conservative in your *"Mirror, Mirror"* exercise, do this in the dark and engage your auditory sense before you engage your visual sense. Instead, please turn on your music and lean into it. Move to the music. Dance like no one's watching—well, because they aren't.

Keep trying this until you don't feel ridiculous. This could take some time. Instead, allow yourself the grace to get to your level of readiness and acceptance.

Work from the darkness to candlelight to those bright 100-watt-age levels when you hit your stride with this exercise. I know that it can be so fricking awkward and forced. It's a very private exercise, and you don't need an audience while doing this unless you want one. (If so, be sure it's someone who will be supportive and encouraging. You can ask them to say positive things to you or just witness in peaceful quiet.)

Don't get disheartened and give up. You've got to be your own cheerleader. Think about what your body has accomplished already, no matter your age. (Refer to your WW# for a refresher.) Your body is an extraordinary machine, a divine temple, or both, so be grateful for how it has carried you to this point.

Keep going on this as often as you need to until you believe it and it is no longer awkward. I suspect this will be one of those ongoing exercises you might need throughout your life. I don't think you will find it a "one-and-done" event.

I wish I had known of this when I was a teenager; that's when all those self-deprecating thoughts about my body started. This also would have been helpful post-pregnancies when my body had morphed through such extraordinary changes. Incidentally, I loved my body during my pregnancies. The total miracle of it all was never lost on me.

Now that I am officially in menopause, it has become mandatory. I'm not going to lie; this still feels awkward sometimes. But much less so. I realize now that all I can do is continue to try and love my body as it is right now, and I hope you do the same.

I am not an expert in the *"Mirror, Mirror"* technique, just a disciple of the approach. I may forget it for a bit, but I always return to it because it works.

I have chosen quite a long list of music selections because I suspect you will need to try a few different tunes to get you in the zone for this exercise. Here are my suggested "Mirror, Mirror" music selections:

"STUCK WITH U" —Ariana Grande and Justin Bieber
If this song doesn't get you feeling all sultry and sexy, I
am out of touch with reality. Or you are. Just kidding.
Justin is a fellow Canadian. Even though I'm 64, I
am a "Belieber." (That's not creepy, is it? I hope not!)
"I love you, Justin... and I'm glad I said it first."

"SEÑORITA" —Shawn Mendes, Camila Cabello
Hoping once again that I don't come across as a creepy
fan, but ditto for the above comments. Honestly,
I'm not stalking under-40 rock stars. I like their
music. I think you will too. *¡Señoras, de nada!*

"NOTHIN' ON YOU" —Cody Johnson
This song is about looking good with nothing on, so
I included it. Just say, *"Why, thank you, Cody."*

Here are a few more playful songs: I recommend you sing
along. *Par-tay!*

"BOOTYLICIOUS" —Destiny's Child
Oh, come on! You know why I chose this one.

"DANCING QUEEN" —Abba
Go dance and have the time of your life, you Dancing Queen!

"BEAUTIFUL U R" —Deborah Cox
Another Canadian Queen. Ms. Cox reminds us
not to let anyone bring us down. Look in that
mirror and see who you are. Beautiful U R!

"SEXYBACK" —Justin Timberlake and Timbaland
Go bring sexy back, girl!

And you know to choose your own music if the above selections don't appeal to you, right? You do you.

Remember that we all know you have already watched yourself dancing by now. This is just taking it to a different level. You got this, girl! You are BeYOUtiful!

CHAPTER 40

Your Self-Care Toolkit

Forgiveness

*T*his is, without a doubt, one of the best Superpowers I have learned. I highly recommend that you get on this one as soon as you finish reading this chapter. This one is a game changer. I have learned that forgiveness will set you free.

I suspect you might ask yourself, *"What does forgiveness have to do with aging?"* That is a fantastic question.

This was a huge "Wish I knew then, what I know now" lesson for me. I was late to the Forgiveness Party in life, meaning I had held on to some baggage and trauma for far too long. Holding onto this was toxic energy, and it weighed me down.

I also became aware that even in some cases where I thought I had moved past something, I hadn't. That was because I had not truly forgiven those who had hurt me, and more importantly, I also had to learn to forgive myself for those I had hurt and for my choices.

I believe that the emotional angst I'd been carrying around contributed to my stress levels through the years. Our emotional well-being and mental health have a WW# all their own that funnels into our physical WW# (Part II, Chapter 17), affecting our aging journey.

The Mayo Clinic confirmed this:

"Letting go of grudges and bitterness can make way for improved health and peace of mind. Forgiveness can lead to the following:

- Healthier relationships
- Improved mental health
- Less anxiety, stress, and hostility
- Lower blood pressure
- Fewer symptoms of depression
- A strong immune system
- Improved heart health
- Improved self-esteem." [47]

"The act of forgiveness offers you both a mental and physical reset."

I discovered that one of the hardest things in life is dealing with the pain of being wrongfully treated (no matter the circumstances) without an apology and knowing that an apology will never come. I certainly know that feeling, and I suspect those I have hurt without an apology also know the feeling.

I learned to let go of anger, much of which I had been harbouring for years.

How did I do that? First, the passage of time has helped to soften the edges of those challenging situations I went through. More importantly, I chose to forgive myself and those with whom I had some issues. I forgave them, not because I condoned what they did, but because the forgiveness was for me. Second, I no longer carried around the hurt and anger inside me.

"As long as you don't forgive, who and whatever it is will occupy rent-free space in your mind."
—ISABELLE HOLLAND

I recall an Oprah Winfrey episode with Iyanla Vanzant where Ms. Vanzant was the first person I had ever heard talk about forgiveness as a powerful mechanism to bolster our emotional health and well-being. She talked about how it allows you to reclaim your power as a forgiver. I was captivated by her (I still am) and sought her out online to learn more from her.

I invite you to connect with her via her website or YouTube. There is nothing I can teach you about forgiveness that would surpass what Ms. Vanzant can teach you.

I can, however, vouch for her methodology and share some pointers. I took it upon myself to build my highly customized version of one of Iyanla Vanzant's exercises, and I call upon this depending on my circumstances. I call this my *"IV Therapy."* And no, I am not trying to claim Ms. Vanzant's work as my own.

Instead, I call it "IV Therapy" because she was the first person I had ever stopped and paid attention to about the topic of forgiveness. She taught me how the act of forgiveness is not for the benefit of the one who hurt you, but instead, it is for you—just learning that alone felt therapeutic, and hence, the name "IV Therapy" for her initials.

How had I not grasped this concept when I was younger? Until then, holding a grudge against someone was like a test of willpower, a sign of strength, and it felt almost like a competition against the "*grudgee*." Until I discovered that I was the only one in the contest and it was just wasting my energy. Trust me; no one is thinking about you like you think they are. Everyone has their own sh*t they're working through.

I learned that I first needed to give myself an emotional tox screen (a mental review) to discover what people, places or things from my past were lurking in my shadows. Unfortunately, this was difficult to cull out because some of it had been buried for a long time.

To get in the zone, I would turn on my music. I didn't have Alexa back then, but I had a great iPod™ playlist (are those even around anymore?) when I started doing IV Therapy.

I would queue up my playlist. "Purple Rain" by Prince gets me in the mental zone for something like this. Then I would get out my journal and start making notes and naming names. I will forewarn you that you won't get a full audit the first time around. It took several sessions to build my list. Layers. I had some unpacking to do.

Once I brought all my demons from my past up to the surface, the real work began. I am talking about demons like guilt, shame, anger, fear, grudges, blame, emotional pain, and trauma I had undergone (and delivered). It was quite a 'To Do" list.

One of the best exercises I used was mentally rebuilding the moment when I had the hurt inflicted on me. Only this time, I had my chance to take the floor. It's like a post-situation visualization exercise. I pretend that the individual, the "perpetrator" (if I can get all Dick Tracey on you), is sitting across from me in my living room, and I pretend that the perp has duct tape over their mouth and has no choice but to hear what I have to say.

By the way, this is my unique addition to my IV Therapy. I am 100% confident Ms. Vanzant does not include duct tape in her methodology. Keep in mind that this is not intended to replace or diminish Ms. Vanzant's work. She is the Goddess of Forgiveness.

Then it is my turn to say whatever I want to my (pretend) perp. Then I push out all my anger. I say the things that I wish I had been able to say out loud.

This brilliant exercise gives you the power to discharge all your pent-up anger and venom directed at the pr*ck who caused you so much pain.

Say all those things you wish you had said, wanted to say; only this time, you get in the last word. Get it all out: scream, cry, cuss, or shout it out. The point of this exercise is to let all that anger out of yourself.

Do not do this on a live person. Please get guidance from a professional if you feel a face-to-face interaction is the way to go. You can also do this as a kind of "role play" in therapy.

I cannot tell you how cathartic my IV Therapy has been. It allowed me to move past the hurt and pain previously inflicted on me.

Forgiveness doesn't necessarily take away the pain, nor does the pain heal instantly. It takes time. You can only go through the forgiveness and healing process when ready. Please don't force it. You will know when it is time. And do it at your own pace. Don't try to heal fifteen incidents at once.

I also discovered that some perps that you thought you had forgiven sometimes come back into your thoughts again, unexpectedly, like some paranormal episode. Somehow, the memory still haunts you, usually after something triggers it. Then I know I must take time to do another round of IV Therapy. So I journal it out and then get into my DF or DM energy (depending on the situation) and get it all out.

Conversely, I am also aware that there are people whom I have hurt. Several people have seen, heard, and felt the worst in me. I am not proud of that. So I learned how to shine the warm light of forgiveness onto myself.

So I also have talked to myself out loud, replaying the scene where I have said some hurtful things to others (where I was the pr*ck). What changed is that I injected what I *"would-a, should-a, could-a"* said or done, and where I forgive myself. I don't want to carry that shame and embarrassment with me, and I have finally given myself grace and self-forgiveness for the hurt I have inflicted on others in the heat of the moment.

I learned to stop shackling myself to my mistakes and mishaps; after all, they're in my personal history books now. I cannot rewrite my past, so I have chosen to own it.

But I don't live there.

I know that I am not a perfect human being, and although I hold myself to a high standard, I have come to realize that only *Deadpool*™ himself is infallible.

The act of forgiveness is a Superpower. It amps your power and elevates how you present yourself in the world. It builds up your self-worth and self-confidence. It clears the toxicity out of your mind, heart, and body. Do not underestimate its power to clear emotional baggage out of your soul.

Forgiveness of myself and others has allowed me to eliminate the emotional burdens, so I don't have to drag them into my 3rd Trimester.

Going through the practice of forgiveness was game changing, cathartic, and massively liberating for me.

> *"Letting go does not mean that you have given up. And it does not mean that you no longer care. It just means that you are releasing the attachments of the past that get in the way of your happiness and mental clarity.*
>
> *Letting go is the unbinding and disentangling of old behaviour patterns that pull you into unnecessary mental tension and worry. When you can be okay*

*with things not having gone a certain way, life begins
again. Making peace with the past opens you up
to love and adventure and allows you to apply the
lessons you have learned with a new calmness."*

—DEAN BOKHARI

Words of Wisdom: I suspect we all have some baggage still spinning around on the "Baggage Claim of Life" that we need to pick up and deal with. Unpack it. What do you have to lose by giving IV Therapy a try? Or do the deep forgiveness work in your own way. Get support if you need to. Liberate yourself from your past hurts. Don't let "it" work you—you work "it" out.

Give yourself some time to get through this—it might take a few sessions, weeks, or even months. Exorcisms can take time. Godspeed.

Disclaimer: Keep in mind that this is my version of what has worked for me. Please review Ms. Vanzant's material and find your path forward.

*"When you can tell the story, and it doesn't
bring up any pain, you know it is healed."*

—IYANLA VANZANT

"Sorry Seems to be the Hardest Word" —Elton John
You know why I chose this song.

"Forgiveness" —Matthew West
It can clear the bitterness away, and the
prisoner it sets free is you.

"ASHES" —Celine Dion

This is one of those "grab your soul" beautiful songs.
She sang this song for the "Deadpool 2" [48] movie.

CHAPTER 41

Your Self-Care Toolkit

Music

I am sure it is evident that music always has played a significant supporting role in my life. I don't believe I could have authored this book without building in the references to the songs I chose to represent and enhance my stories and life.

It's incredible how a song can transport me to a time and place when that song was like a placeholder for an event in my life.

How beautiful is that connection? I am assuming this happens to you, too.

All the music, lyrics, and artists I referenced in these pages mean something to me. In some cases, their lyrics fit the story I was telling, while in other cases, the songs moved me and are symbolic of how I have felt or currently feel.

I recognize that all of my music selections may not be to your taste, so build up your unique playlist to serve as a backdrop to your own Hero's Journey. What songs would you choose to complement your life?

"I Write the Songs" —Barry Manilow
Remember this one? Let Barry's smooth-as-silk vocals wash over you. Life is a worldwide symphony, so let music fill your heart.

"What a Song Should Do" —Tim Hicks
Giddy up! Music should make you dance, make you think, make you dance some more, and shout out *"Hell yeah, me too!"*

CHAPTER 42

Your Self-Care Toolkit
Summary

PART VI SUMMARY

Please make time to check in with your inner self regularly. If you are a good meditator, I anticipate that you are already in tune with yourself.

I am not a consistent meditator, so I have found other ways to engage my inner self and undertake a self-audit of my feelings about where I am on my life path. I have come to rely on these tools to guide me through the lumps and bumps along the road.

I do not have any coaching, medical, or other professional designations that might bolster my credibility with these tools. I can only tell you that they have worked for me.

I am not some Goody Two-Shoes (*is that still a thing?*) that believes my life is all light, love and Lululemons™; not even close. I still have sh*tty days where I feel like staying in bed watching Netflix. Some days I really do this!

I still have occasions when I want to tell a few people to f*ck off, and I will only if necessary, but these days, it's rare. Conversely, I am sure some people would also like to tell me to f*ck off. Probably more often than I realize. *W-h-a-t-e-v-e-r!* I've gone through the Rhett Butler Portal, remember?

I am not under any illusion that I have made it to the Promised Land. I am still on my Hero's Journey and forever will be a student and work in progress.

My 2 Cents' Worth

BACKGROUND FOR PART VII:

How is this for a sobering statistic?

"Canada ranks right in the middle of the pack among G20 countries for poverty among people aged 65-plus, according to 2021 data from the Organization for Economic Cooperation and Development.

In a June online survey of 1,515 Canadians by Angus Reid, four out of ten said they delayed retirement because they have too much debt, while 62% delayed it because they don't have enough savings and investments." [49]

Don't gloss over this section, no matter your age. This one's extremely important!

CHAPTER 43

She Works Hard for the Money

*S*tatistically speaking, I am going to live longer than my parents. My father passed away when he was 54, and my mother passed away at 86. If I live out to current Canadian statistics, I will likely reach my 90s. Statistically, my children also are expected to live even longer than me.

You cannot start early enough to prepare yourself financially for your later years. I know that if you're in your 1st Trimester of Life, you may not be thinking about this because having fun is top of mind. That's okay. You can still have fun and enjoy your youth, but my strongest advice is don't wait on this.

Ask yourself a few questions right now, no matter your age:

- Do you know precisely where your monthly income goes?
- How much do you save monthly?
- Where and how do you save your money?
- Are you personally involved in managing your finances?

It would be best if you were personally involved in this critical area of your life. Please do not surrender this power to others. I cannot emphasize enough the importance of this. Don't be complacent; take control of your finances.

Educate yourself in all matters relating to your wealth, insurance, debts, investments, and possessions. This means whether you have two cents or a bazillion dollars, be it in real estate, cash, bank accounts, stocks, bonds, cryptocurrency, safety deposit boxes, property or vehicle ownership, art, jewellery, your Pokémon card collection, intellectual property, or any financial wealth.

Be personally and directly involved in all matters of individual and jointly held monetary resources. If assets are jointly owned and managed electronically, ensure you know the passcodes and log in regularly. Ensure you have a copy of all the paperwork for these resources and a set of keys to any lockboxes, safes, and safety deposit boxes. Know where the coffee can filled with cash is buried in your backyard.

Be sure to have a written will. I am not trying to pass myself off as a legal advisor, but I suggest you and your partner have up-to-date wills and powers of attorney for both financial and medical.

A Certified Financial Planner (CFP) will tell you these things, and so will well-written books on personal finance. So unless you are a bona fide financial guru who manages your finances expertly with a winning track record, I highly suggest you connect with someone who is. Do this independently or jointly with your significant other ASAP if you haven't already done so. And if it's been years since you've had a financial wellness checkup, schedule another one. I'm serious.

Get a good one. Shop around and get someone with impeccable references, high reviews online and no scam alerts, a successful history, and a deep customer base. Find one you trust and whom you connect with, someone who is aligned with and supportive of your life goals—and not just their commission rate.

Words of Wisdom: First things first. When dealing with your finances, you must get into your DM (Bo$$ energy). Own this. Get intimately involved with your financial affairs. Don't abdicate your throne here, Queen.

Recall that we are all likely to live longer than our parents. So it would be best if you started planning as early as yesterday for your financial future.

Work out a plan for financing your retirement as soon as you start working. I'm not kidding.

None of us know what the future holds. I fully understand that if you are currently under 30, you probably feel invincible, and retirement feels so far off.

If that's you, unless you have a significant guaranteed trust fund coming your way, you probably will be working longer than I had to. I suspect the Canadian Federal Government will eventually push back on Old Age Security eligibility since it's currently at a 65-year retirement age (here in Canada).

In the United States, I understand their Social Security benefits can start as early as 62 years of age, but the U.S. government now considers 67 the "full retirement age."

In Canada and the U.S., the earlier-than-full-retirement age pensioners will get a reduced benefit compared to those who wait until full retirement age.

When I was in my 20s, I thought I had plenty of time to figure out the details about my future, retirement, and everything. Looking back, I was so naïve. Earlier is better. Time moves very quickly. Don't sleep on this.

Words of Wisdom: I am not a financial expert, so I hired one. While my wealth is not off the charts, I am doing fine and can sustain myself through my remaining 40+ years. Do the math. I'm planning on going from "sexagenarian" to "centenarian." I want to be a Queenager.

There are some incredibly reliable resources and people who are experts in the world of personal finance. Ask your friends whom they recommend.

This decision is as crucial to your future financial well-being as SPF is to your future skin.

"What's in your Wallet?"™

"SHE WORKS HARD FOR THE MONEY" —Donna Summer
You work hard for your money, so they better treat you
right. And you'd better treat your money right, too.

"R.E.S.P.E.C.T." —Aretha Franklin
There is a reason this is *Rolling Stone* magazine's
#1 song of the Top 500 Songs. Get it, girrrrl!

"9 TO 5" —Dolly Parton
You're caught up in the same routine,
Working hard but life's not what it seems.
You know there's more to this than just a grind,
So take a chance, let your dreams unwind!

CHAPTER 44

What's Love Got To Do With It?

*D*o you know who Suze Orman is? If not, *"Suze Orman is an American financial advisor, author, and podcast host. Ms. Orman has written ten consecutive New York Times bestsellers about personal finance. She was named twice to the Time 100 list of influential people and has won two Emmy Awards and eight Gracie Awards."* [50]

Someone challenged Ms. Orman on the need for prenuptial agreements, indicating that they felt prenups were a sign of distrust in a love relationship. Here is what Ms. Orman had to say about that:

"Time for a reality check, my friends. First, drawing up a prenuptial agreement together is a sign of incredible trust and financial openness—you are fooling yourself if you think you can achieve complete intimacy without it." [51]

I completely agree with Ms. Orman. If nuptials aren't in the equation, but living together is, both partners considering these types of life-altering situations still need to protect themselves and their respective financial worth and resources through legal documentation, such as a prenup and/or cohabitation agreement before you make it all happen.

"Love is a many splendored thing,
but so is your money."

"WHAT'S LOVE GOT TO DO WITH IT" —Tina Turner
No explanation is required for why I chose this song, but
I think Ms. Orman would agree with my selection.

CHAPTER 45

Your Little Black Book (LBB)

A Little Black Book sounds intriguing, doesn't it?

In the olden days, an "LBB" was a private listing of some of our most favoured acquaintances that we could call upon for a guaranteed good time. (*wink, wink*) Of course, our cell phones can now serve up any good time imaginable, so perhaps the "LBB" has gone out of fashion. However, I have another use for an LBB that I will share with you.

Not to get all morbid on you, but my LBB is a three-ring binder full of relevant and required information that my children will need to get my funeral wishes conducted and my estate underway.

I built my LBB after my divorce; I return to it occasionally to ensure the information is still relevant and up to date for my children in the event of my death.

It contains:

- Will and powers of attorney (for financial and medical decisions)
- Copies (or originals) of all relevant personal identification documents (birth certificate, Social Insurance Number, passport, Nexus, health card, driver's license, etc.)
- Copies of all my financial information—financial institutions, account numbers, credit cards, stock portfolio, RSP portfolio, points cards, redemptions, etc.
- Location of deeds, property tax roll information, utility information
- Passcodes/passwords
- My funeral wishes, information for any prepaid burial plot or services, and insurance information
- Data for the distribution of my personal effects, not covered by my will
- Lawyer, contact information for my family, and my Certified Financial Planner

I won't minimize for you the amount of time that this took to pull together, but I also won't underestimate the value of this book—for my children, not just myself.

My children know of my LBB's existence and where to find it in the event of my death.

Words of Wisdom: I know we all have that "LBD" in our closets; I highly recommend you add an LBB for your family for estate purposes. Get into your DM energy and make it happen.

"LITTLE BLACK DRESS" —One Direction
This song has nothing to do with an LBB but everything to do with an LBD. It's a female thing. You knew I had to include it. So go put on your LBD and red shoes, perhaps? to dance to this one.

CHAPTER 46

"Money, Money, Money"

—ABBA

PART VII SUMMARY

I don't think I need to keep driving home my point here. I can only suggest that you consider your financial holdings seriously and prepare for your future as best as possible.

Do your loved ones a favour and leave them your LBB. They will be so grateful that you took the time to build it for them. But be sure to tell them where to find it in the event of your death. Having a complete LBB is also really helpful for your own peace of mind.

Indeed, money is essential, but I still believe the best things in life are free.

"Money, Money, Money" —ABBA
Like they sing, "It changes everything."

And Then A Hero Comes Along

BACKGROUND FOR PART VIII:

"One day it just clicks...

You realize what's important and what isn't. You learn to care less about what other people think of you and more about what you think of yourself.

You realize how far you've come and remember when you thought things were such a mess that you would never recover. And you smile. You smile because you are truly proud of yourself and the person you've fought to become.

—YUNG PUEBLO

This is so beautifully and honestly said. There is nothing I need to add to it. Read it again.

CHAPTER 47

It's My Life. It's Now or ?

*A*s I get older, I have become more entrenched in my values and firmer in my convictions of what I stand for. At the same time, I have become less tolerant of ignorance in people, but that's likely in part due to my genetics—my mom didn't tolerate fools gladly. I don't care too much about what others think anymore. My passing years have emboldened me.

It is not lost on me that I may not always enjoy good health as I wade farther into my future. I know that more physical, mental, and emotional markers will reveal themselves over time. I am as ready as I can be to take them on and assimilate them into my life.

My intention on retirement was to go hard for the first ten years to work through my Life List. I don't call it a "Bucket List" because to me, that implies death is imminent (as in "kicking the bucket.") I want to go on adventures and burn through my stash of Aeroplan™ miles to travel to all the places I want to go.

I want to take risks and jump into new activities. This sense of abandonment and risk-taking also pushed me to write this book. Have I felt out of my depth while doing so? Absolutely. I stopped and started several times.

But I pushed back on the fear and kept writing; what did I have to lose? Writing and researching this book kept me contentedly distracted and purposeful through the Pandemic and beyond. And like I said earlier, I am taking a risk, baby. So that's what I have committed to doing in my 3rd Trimester of Life.

I will now share with you a list of what I will choose to do as I move forward through the rest of my life. I recognize this is a *highly ambitious* listing, but it helps me focus and have things to look forward to, so I commit to it. The Pandemic took about two years out of my ten-year plan, so I am in catch-up mode.

I will need to come back and revisit this listing to keep myself on the True North trajectory I have set for myself. I hope this list inspires some ideas of your own. And, of course, your list will be different.

- I will own and honour my past but not live there.
- I will authentically and unapologetically be myself.
- I don't know what my future holds. I know what I want to

build into my future, and my Vision Board, manifestations and goal setting will help keep me on track.

- I will lean into my life with excitement.
- I will remember that I am free to write the rest of my story and free to change it.
- I will celebrate myself and my WW#.
- In my 3rd Trimester of Life, I will deploy the knowledge and wisdom I have acquired.
- I will embody the Superpowers I have earned so far and know more lessons will come.
- I will wear my Invisibility Cloak if and when I choose to.
- I will keep my physical body and health in shape (as I define it).
- I will keep my emotional and mental health in a constant levelling-up process.
- I will continue to try and live in the "now."
- I will try to let go of perfectionism. No fixing is required. I have learned it is safe to be all of me as I am.
- I will continue to love myself, with all my imperfections.
- I will make myself a priority and show up for myself.
- I will continue to enjoy my dark chocolate, my Santa Margherita™ Pinot Grigio (yup—the good stuff), the occasional bag of dill pickle potato chips and an occasional A&W™ Teen Burger (deliciously nostalgic).
- I will continue to enjoy my music and build up my playlists, and dance if I want to, whenever, wherever, and however I want to.
- I will throw out all the negative self-talk because I deserve better from myself.

- I will gracefully and gratefully accept compliments and not deflect them.
- I will go on all the adventures I can.
- I will continue to take risks (that won't harm me or others, of course).
- I will continue to enjoy the little things: my first cup of coffee on my patio, reading my first email of the day from the "Universe" (see Appendix B for the link), and digging around in my garden. All these things mean so much more to me now than they ever did.
- I don't need big grand things to make me happy. I love my Louboutins™, but the simple things in life have always meant the most to me. They still do.
- I will show up however I want to show up and present myself to the world without adapting to others' expectations of me.
- I will pamper myself and be surrounded by my favourite things—my family first and forever.
- As an introvert who is a situational extrovert, I will take the time I need to recharge my batteries.
- My home is my haven, and it reflects who I am. It is where I cocoon to recharge my batteries. I will keep my home safe, warm, and welcoming for myself, my family, and my friends.
- I will do my best to age with acceptance, integrity, and grace.
- I will do my absolute best to accept all the changes that will continue to happen to me and around me. I will take the necessary steps to offset, minimize, and lean into these changes.
- I will be present on any social media platforms of my choosing.

- I will continue to use, balance, and express my DF and DM energies.
- I will continue using my Self-Care Toolkit tools when needed.
- Should the going get tough, I will continue to remember that things happen for me; they don't happen to me. And I will find my way to the other side—I always have.

Words of Wisdom: Last one! Aging is a long, gradual, and never-ending process. Look around; no one is getting any younger—this is a universal phenomenon.

If you are struggling with the aging process, then redefine it. Rewire your negative thoughts on aging. Honour the emotions and the feelings that have come along for the ride. Consider all the benefits and strengths you have earned already.

> *"I have learned that aging is not only a privilege but also an opportunity."*

If you didn't believe that on the first page of this book, I hope now that you have joined me in this understanding. Don't be afraid—lean into it. You are responsible for finding ways to help yourself enjoy the ride.

- Be your own best friend—don't bully yourself. (This one's not easy.)
- Stay relevant and be aware of the world; participate in it as you want. What lights you up? Follow that fire and your passions.

- Celebrate yourself, your WW#, and the wisdom you have picked up along the way.
- Get rid of any toxic energy or baggage from the past. Don't carry that negative energy around you. Exorcise that sh*t out. Exercise too if you want. Seriously—find ways to liberate yourself.
- Look for the silver linings and lessons from your own life's adventures. What have you learned? How have you grown?
- Invest in yourself as you define it. What should that look like? Level up, glow up, stand up. You deserve it. Make it a part of your own self-love story.
- Just as Lee Ann Womack sings, "I Hope You Dance."
- Know and own your inherent worthiness.
- Accept compliments.
- You have built up Superpowers, so flex them and continue to build them.
- You are a woman.
- You are a warrior.
- It's Your Life.
- You. Got. This.
- Grab your hairbrush microphone, get in front of your full-length mirror, crank up the volume, and sing along with these songs. Make some noise! I know you want to. Rock on—it's now or never!

"HERO" —Mariah Carey
Find your strength and superpowers within.
I promise you, they're there.

"I HOPE YOU DANCE" —Lee Ann Womack
Just dance.

"IT'S MY LIFE" —Bon Jovi
Just live! It's Now or ?

I sincerely thank you for taking time from your busy life to read about some of the adventures, trials, and tribulations that shaped my Hero's Journey.

I hope you found some useful information that will help you on yours. Please refer to this book should you ever need a reminder to keep loving yourself at every age and stage of your life. I promise you are worth it!

Now, it's your turn...

Ms. Corrine Bailey Rae would suggest you let your hair down, put your records on, and play your favourite songs.

I suggest you also get even more comfortable, put on your harem pants, (wear 'em if you got 'em!) and take your bra off 'cause you're home. Get yourself a beautiful journal, in the format of your choice, and write on, sister!

Then pour a nice beverage, lean into your music, and lean into yourself.

Write your story. *C'est Magnifique!*

If you enjoyed my book, I would be so grateful if you would leave me feedback on Amazon™ and consider gifting it to the women you know.

Better yet, bring it to your next monthly book club to share with your closest friends!

Please feel free to stay in touch. All of my contact information is listed at the front of the book.

Brenda

"THIS IS ME" —Keala Seattle & The Greatest Showman Ensemble
This song is all about empowerment. Own it. Make no apologies. Say it out loud, "This Is Me!"

My Notes

Music and Artist Listing

(In Order of Appearance in Book)

ARTIST	SONG	PUBLISHER
Miley Cyrus	The Climb	John Shanks, March 5, 2009
Ed Sheeran	Supermarket Flowers	Benny Blanco, Johnny McDaid, Mar. 3 2017
will.i.am.	I Got it From My Mama	will.i.am, July 31, 2007
Christina Aguilera	I Turn to You	Guy Roche, February 13, 2020
Luke Combs	Six Feet Apart	Luke Combs, Chip Matthews, May 1, 2020
The Beatles	With a Little Help from My Friends	Song/ATV Music Publishing, 1967
Bruno Mars	Count on Me	The Smeezingtons, November 7, 2011
The Rembrandts	I'll Be There For You	East West America-Elektra. May 23, 1995
Kesha	TiK ToK	Dr. Luke, Benny Blanco, August 7, 2009
Bebe Rexha	Not 20 Anymore	Monsters & Strangers, August 30, 2019

ARTIST	SONG	PUBLISHER
Patsy Cline	Crazy	Owen Bradley, October, 1961
Maroon 5 and Christina Aguilera	Moves Like Jagger	Shellback; Benny Blanco, June 21, 2011
Bee Gees	Night Fever	Robert Stigwood, December 12, 1977
Adele	Easy on Me	Greg Kurstin, October 15, 2021
David Bowie	Changes	Ken Scott, David Bowie, January 7, 1972
Lizzo	Good as Hell	Ricky Reed, March 8, 2016
Cyndi Lauper	Girls Just Want to Have Fun	Rick Chertoff, William Wittman, September 6, 1983
Lighthouse	Sunny Days	Jimmy Lenner, November 1972
Sheryl Crowe	Soak Up The Sun	Sheryl Crow, Jeff Trott, February 11, 2022
The Beatles	When I'm 64	George Martin, May 26, 1967
Rod Stewart	You Wear It Well	Mercury, August, 1972
Electric Light Orchestra	Telephone Line	Jet Records and United Artists, May, 1977
Johnny Nash	I Can See Clearly Now	Johnny Nash, July 1972
Louis Armstrong	What a Wonderful World	Bob Thiele, September 1, 1967
Willie Nelson	Dusty Bottles	Buddy Cannon, April 22, 2022

ARTIST	SONG	PUBLISHER
Doobie Brothers	Listen to the Music	Ted Templeman, July 19, 1972
Ciara	Level Up	J.R. Rotem, July 17, 2018
John Mellencamp	Hurts So Good	John Mellencamp, Don Gehman, April 1982
Geri Halliwell	It's Raining Men	Stephen Lipson, 2001
Elton John	The Bitch is Back	Gus Dudgeon, September 3, 1974
Nelly	Hot in Here	The Neptunes, May 7, 2002
Alicia Keys	Girl on Fire	Alicia Keys, Jeff Bhasker, Salaam Remi, September 4, 2012
Tina Turner	I Don't Wanna Lose You	Roger Davies, 1989
Tori Kelly	Dear No One	Nicole Acacio, John Latham, November 6, 2013
Chris Stapleton	Tennessee Whiskey	Dave Cobb, Chris Stapleton, 2015
Ronnie McDowell	Older Women	Buddy Killen, June, 1981
John Mayer	Gravity	John Mayer, Steve Jordan, September 12, 2006
Miranda Lambert	Gravity is a B*tch	Sony/ATV Music Publishing 2014
Jax	Victoria's Secret	Jesse Siebenberg, Mark Nilan, June 30, 2022

ARTIST	SONG	PUBLISHER
Alessia Cara	Scars to Your Beautiful	Pop & Oak, Coleridge Tillman and DJ Frank E, November 13, 2015
Cher	If I Could Turn Back Time	Guy Roche, Diane Warren, March 9, 1999
Andra Day	Rise Up	Lisa Dondlinger, 2015
Shania Twain	Man I Feel Like a Woman	Robert John Lang, March, 1999
Bob Seger & The Silver Bullet Band	Against the Wind	Bill Szymczyk, April 1980
Rachel Platten	Fight Song	John Levine, May 12. 2015
Sam Cooke	A Change is Gonna Come	Hugo & Luigi, January 30, 1964
Hunter Hayes	Invisible	Hunter Hayes, Dan Huff, 2014
Solomon Burke	Cry to Me	Bert Berns, 1962
Christina Aguilera	Beautiful	Linda Perry, November 16, 2012
Bruno Mars	Just the Way You Are	The Smeezingtons, Needlz, July 20, 2010
Katy Perry	Roar	Dr. Luke Max Martin Cirkut, August 10, 2013
Taylor Swift	Mean	Taylor Swift, Nathan Chapman, March 13, 2011
Taylor Swift	Shake It Off	Max Martin, Shellback, August 19, 2014

ARTIST	SONG	PUBLISHER
Kelly Clarkson	Stronger	Greg Kurstin, 2011
Bob Dylan	Forever Young	Rob Fraboni, January 17, 1974
Rod Stewart	Forever Young	Rod Stewart, Andy Taylor, July, 1988
One Direction	Night Changes	Julian Bunetta, John Ryan, November 14, 2014
James Blunt	You're Beautiful	Tom Rothrock, May 30, 2005
Fleetwood Mac	Landslide	Fleetwood Mac, Keith Olsen, 1975
Meghan Trainor	All About That Bass	Kevin Kadish, June 30, 2014
Katy Perry	Firework	Stargate Sandy Vee, October 26, 2010
Toby Keith	As Good As I Once Was	James Stroud, Toby Keith, May 9, 2005
Martina McBride	This One's For the Girls	Martina McBride, Paul Worley, June 9, 2003
Whitney Houston	Greatest Love of All	Michael Masser, June, 1977
Taylor Swift, featuring Brendon Urie of Panic! At the Disco)	ME!	Taylor Swift, Joel Little, April 6, 2019
Lady Gaga	Born This Way	Lady Gaga, Fernando Garibay, Jeppe Laursen, DJ White Shadow, February 11, 2011

ARTIST	SONG	PUBLISHER
Frank Sinatra	My Way	Sonny Burke, March, 1969
Eminem	Lose Yourself	Eminem, Jeff Bass, Luis Resto, October 28, 2022
Bachman-Turner-Overdrive	Takin' Care of Business	Randy Bachman, January, 1974
Jann Arden	Good Mother	Universal Songs of Polygram International, 1994
Bee Gees	Stayin' Alive	Bee Gees, Albhy Galuten, Karl Richardson, December, 1977
Poison	Every Rose Has Its Thorn	Tom Werman, October 12, 1988
Gloria Gaynor	I Will Survive	Freddie Perren, Dino Fekaris, October 23, 1978
Helen Reddy	I Am Woman	Jay Senter, May, 1972
Taylor Swift	Lover	Jack Antonoff, Taylor Swift, August 16, 2019
Creedence Clearwater Revival	I Put a Spell on You	Saul Zaentz, 1972
Demi Lovato	Confident	Max Martin, Ilya, September 18, 2015
Sia	Unstoppable	Jesse Shatkin, January 21, 2016
Jewel	Intuition	Lester Mendez, Jewel Kilcher, April 7, 2003
Sarah Bareilles	Brave	Mark Endert, 2013
Neil Diamond	I Am...I Said	Tom Catalano, March 15, 1971

ARTIST	SONG	PUBLISHER
Emmy Meli	I AM WOMAN	Okano, November 18, 2021
Prince	Purple Rain	Prince and the Revolution, June 25, 1984
Corrine Bailey Rae	Put Your Records On	Steve Chrisanthou, Jimmy Hogarth, February 20, 2006
Maren Morris	My Church	busbee, Maren Morris, January 19, 2016
Natasha Bedingfield	Unwritten	Wayne Rodrigues, Danielle Brisbois, November 29, 2004
Billie Eilish	bad guy	Finneas O'Connell, March 29, 2019
Ariana Grande & Justin Bieber	Stuck With U	Freddy Wexler, Gian Stone, Ariana Grande, May 8, 2020
Shawn Mendes & Camila Cabelo	Señorita	Andrew Watt, Benny Blanco, Cashmere Cat, June 21, 2019
Cody Johnson	Nothin' on You	Trent Willmon, 2019
Destiny's Child	Bootylicious	Rob Fusari, Beyonce Knowles, Falonte Moore, May 22, 2001
ABBA	Dancing Queen	Benny Andersson, Bjorn Ulvaeus, August 15, 1976
Deborah Cox	Beautiful U R	The Avila Brothers, Big Jim, September, 2008
Justin Timberlake and Timbaland	SexyBack	Timbaland, Justin Timberlake, Nate "Danja" Hills, July 18, 2006
Elton John	Sorry Seems to Be the Hardest Word	Gus Dudgeon, March 22, 1976

ARTIST	SONG	PUBLISHER
Matthew West	Forgiveness	Peter Kipley, July 10, 2012
Celine Dion	Ashes	Steve Mac, May 3, 2018
Barry Manilow	I Write the Songs	Daryl Dragon, May 23, 1975
Tim Hicks	What a Song Should Do	Jeff Coplan, April 8, 2019
Donna Summer	She Works Hard for the Money	Michael Omartian, 1983
Aretha Franklin	R.E.S.P.E.C.T.	Steve Cropper, 1965
Dolly Parton	"9 to 5"	Greg Perry, November 3, 1980
Tina Turner	What's Love Got to Do With It?	Terry Britten, May, 1984
One Direction	Little Black Dress	Julian Bunetta, John Ryan and Theodore Geiger, November 25, 2013
ABBA	Money, Money, Money	Benny Andersson, Bjorn Ulvaeus, November 1, 1976
Mariah Carey	Hero	Mariah Carey, Walter Afanasieff, October 18, 1993
Lee Ann Womack	I Hope You Dance	Mark Wright, March 2000
Bon Jovi	It's My Life	Jon Bon Jovi, Richie Sambora, Luke Ebbin, May 8, 2000

ARTIST	SONG	PUBLISHER
Keala Settle & The Greatest Showman Ensemble	This is Me	Greg Wells, Justin Paul, Adam Gubman, Alex Lacmoire, December 8, 2017
The Beatles	In My Life	George Martin, December 3, 1965

SCAN THE QR CODE TO ACCESS
"Aging Sucks... But You're Gonna Love It!"
Playlist

Weblinks and
QR Code Links

PAGE	DESCRIPTION	COMPANY/ WEBSITE	QR CODE
46	Neutrogena 360® Assessment	Neutrogena Skin360® Web App	
63	Online Eye Test for Reading Glasses	Reading Glasses Power Finder. Readers.com®	
66	Online Auditory Test	Quick, easy and free online hearing test. Hearing Life Canada	

PAGE	DESCRIPTION	COMPANY/ WEBSITE	QR CODE
71	Cognitive Functioning Test	Test Your Cognitive Function Today— Food for the Brain	
71	Paint by Number Coloring Games *Free* Bird Color Sort Puzzle *Free* Tile Master- Classic Match *Free* June's Journey: Hidden Objects *Free*	Daily Innovation Co., Limited Hang Nguyen Minh, Developer Higgs Technology Co., Limited Wooga GmbH	Download all from the Apple™ App Store
91	Menopause Symptoms and Tracker	The Menopause Foundation of Canada	

PAGE	DESCRIPTION	COMPANY/WEBSITE	QR CODE
91	National Menopause Foundation	Home—National Menopause Foundation	
91	The North American Menopause Society	North American Menopause Society (NAMS)—Focused on Providing Physicians, Practitioners & Women Menopause Information, Help & Treatment Insights	
104	The Body Dysmorphia Test	Body Dysmorphic Disorder Foundation The Body Dysmorphia Test — BDDF (bddfoundation.org)	
142	Educational language programs	Duolingo.com Duolingo— The world's best way to learn a language	

PAGE	DESCRIPTION	COMPANY/ WEBSITE	QR CODE
157	Jane Fonda TED Talk	Jane Fonda: Life's Third Act. TED Talk	
204	"Reinvention" Podcast	Arlene Dickinson Podcast — Arlene Dickinson	
220	What is your Leading Energy? Free Quiz	What's Your Leading Energy? Masculine or Feminine (tonyrobbins.com)	
226	Signal for Help	Canadian Women's Foundation Signal For Help. Use Signal to Ask for Help. Canadian Women's Foundation	

PAGE	DESCRIPTION	COMPANY/ WEBSITE	QR CODE
226	"How to Tune Into and Trust Your Intuition"	Sonia Choquette On How To Tune Into And Trust Your Intuition. YouTube	
294	Notes from the Universe	Notes From The Universe—TUT	

Bibliography

1. *Grace & Frankie,* Skydance Media Productions Company, 2015-2022, Marta Kauffman, Howard J. Morris.
2. "The Fool." TheTarotGuide.com. The Fool Tarot Card Meaning, https://www.thetarotguide.com.
3. Staves, Dana. 2018. "The Best Brené Brown Quotes on Vulnerability, Love, and Belonging." *Book Riot,* April 16, 2018. https://bookriot.com/brene-brown-quotes/.
4. Marie, Victoria, dir. 2020, *Gray Is the New Blonde.*
5. "Skin 360 Personalized Skin Assessment Online." n.d. NEUTROGENA®, accessed June 30, 2022. https://www.neutrogena.ca/skin360.
6. Riew, K. Daniel, MD. New York Presbyterian Hospital. September 16, 2022. "Tips to prevent 'tech neck' and other pain from technology use." https://healthmatters.nyp.org/how-to-prevent-tech-neck/.
7. Schanzlin, David, MD. "Does Everyone Need Reading Glasses Eventually?" September 24, 2021. https://www.presbyopialife.com.
8. "Aging Eyes." *Joy TV,* December 19, 2018. https://www.joytv.ca/video/carpe-diem-aging-eyes.
9. "How Do You Know If Your Sunglasses Are Protecting Your Eyes?" n.d. Iris.ca. Accessed December 29, 2022. https://iris.ca/en/blog-post-detail/how-do-you-know-sunglasses-are-protecting-eyes.

10. "Hearing Loss: A Common Problem for Older Adults."
National Institute on Aging. 2018. https://www.nia.nih.gov/
health/hearing-loss-common-problem-older-adults.

11. "Our Mission & Vision" https://foodforthebrain.org/
food-for-the-brain-mission.

12. "Health Indicators Interactive Tool." n.d. Yourhealthsystem.
cihi.ca. http://yourhealthsystem.cihi.ca/epub.

13. Dickinson, Arlene. 2020. Review of *Reinvention* Podcast.
Venture Communications.

14. "What is Menopause?" National Institute on Aging.
September 30, 2021. https://www.nia.nih.gov/health/
what-menopause#symptoms.

15. "What is Body Dysmorphic Disorder (BDD) or Body
Dysmorphia?" bddfoundation.org.

16. Clancy, Nicole. "How to Recognize Body Dysmorphic
Disorder in Teens." September 11, 2019. *Parent.*

17. "Cellulite: What It Is, Causes and Treatment."
September 30, 2021. https://www.nia.nih.gov/health/
what-menopause#symptoms.

18. *Merriam-Webster.com Dictionary*, s.v. "ageism," accessed
October 15, 2022. https://www.merriam-webster.com/
dictionary/ageism.

19. *Merriam-Webster.com Dictionary*, s.v. "elderly," accessed
October 15, 2022. https://www.merriam-webster.com/
dictionary/elderly.

20. Sporre, Kathy. "Ageism: The Four Types." February 17, 2019.
https://refinedbyage.com/2019/02/17/ageism-the-four-types/.

21. Whaley, Kimberly A. "Ageism and the Law in Canada."
    June 23, 2021. https://doi.org/https://welpartners.com/
    blog/2021/06/ageism-and-the-law-in-canada/.
22. Age Discrimination | U.S. Department of Labor (dol.gov).
23. Gunderson, Morley. "Barriers to the Labour Force
    Participation of Older Workers in Canada." *May 1, 2021.*
    www.fraserinstitute.org.
24. Age Discrimination | U.S. Department of Labor (dol.gov).
25. https://www.fraserinstitute.org/sites/default/files/barriers-to-
    labour-force-participation-of-older-workers-in-canada.pdf.
26. "The One with the Cop." November 1, 2021. *Friends* https://
    en.wikipedia.org/wiki/The_One_with_the_Cop.
27. Miller, George, dir. 2015. *Mad Max* movie.
28. Fonda, Jane. "Life's Third Act." *TED Talk 1325.* https://www.
    ted.com/talks/jane_fonda_life_s_third_act?language=en.
29. Fonda, Jane. 2011. *Prime Time*, Random House
    Publishing Group.
30. Arden, Jann. 2022."Waiting for the Crone," *If I Knew*
    Then: Finding Wisdom in Failure and Power in Aging. S.l.:
    Vintage Canada.
31. *Good Luck to You, Leo Grande*, Searchlight Pictures, 2022.
32. "Older Adults and Population Aging Statistics." August
    22, 2022. https://www.statcan.gc.ca/en/subjects-start/
    older_adults_and_population_aging.
33. U.S. Bureau of Labor Statistics. Older workers: Labor force
    trends and career options: Career Outlook: U.S. Bureau of
    Labor Statistics (bls.gov).
34. Moore, Dene. "The End of Retirement." *Zoomer,*
    August 1, 2022.

35. Mallick, Mita. "#KeeptheGrey Campaign is a Brilliant Example of Showing Up." Adweek.com, September 1, 2022.

36. Mallick, Adweek.com, September 1, 2022.

37. Mallick, Adweek.com, September 1, 2022.

38. Clarke, Caitlin, and Vikki Velasquez. "Baby Boomer: Definition, Years, Date Range, Retirement and Preparation." July 31, 2022 https://www.investopedia.com/terms/b/baby_boomer.asp.

39. Dychtwald, Ken. "Ageism Is Alive and Well in Advertising." September 8, 2022. https://www.aarp.org/work/age-discrimination/ageism-in-advertising/.

40. Dickens, Charles. 1859. *A Tale of Two Cities*, Penguin Books, 1859.

41. J. Pittman McGehee. 2011. *The Paradox of Love*. Bright Sky Publishing.

42. Arden, Jann. "Waiting for the Crone."

43. Harvey, Steve. 2009. *Act Like a Lady, Think Like a Man*. Amistad Press.

44. *Merriam-Webster.com Dictionary*, s.v. "intuition," accessed October 15, 2022. https://www.merriam-webster.com/dictionary/intuition.

45. *Canadian Women's Foundation*, "Download the Signal for Help Responder's Action Guide: Learn How to Help When You See Signs of Gender-Based Violence." n.d. Action—accessed October 16, 2022. https://action.canadianwomen.org/signal-for-help-guide.

46. Dean, Bokhari. "50 Self-Affirmations to Help You Stay Motivated Every Day." https://www.lifehack.org/863537/self-affirmation.

47. "Letting Go of Grudges and Bitterness." https://www.mayo-clinic.org/healthy-lifestyle/adult-health/in-depth/forgiveness/.

48. David, Leitch, dir. 2018. *Deadpool 2*.

49. Moore, Dene, and Morley Gunderson. "The End of Retirement." *Zoomer*, August 1, 2022.

50. "Suze Orman." https://en.wikipedia.org/wiki/Suze_Orman.

51. Megan, Leonhardt. "Here's Why Suze Orman Says You Should Always Get a Prenup." Make It. March 11, 2020. https://www.cnbc.com/2020/03/11/why-suze-orman-says-you-should-always-get-a-prenup.html.

Acknowledgements

First, thank you to my family for your unwavering support. I love you, and I thank you.

Before I brazenly name names below, please know that I am incredibly grateful for how you each inspired me in unique ways.

I want to extend a sincere and genuine thank you to all musicians, artists, entrepreneurs, authors, and actors for your *"unbeknownst-to-you"* contributions to my life and whose work I have shared within these pages. My deepest gratitude goes out to each of you.

Ms. Bebe Rexha, I don't know how to articulate effectively what your song *"Not 20 Anymore"* means to me. I tried to explain it within these pages, yet I still suspect I have short-changed its meaning. Hearing it for the first time was like a gift. It still feels the same way. Thank you for your beautiful work.

Ms. Jane Fonda, thank you for sharing so many of your stories with us and for putting *"your brave on!"* and leading the way with such refinement. And, of course, for the role of Grace Hansen you so fearlessly and brilliantly portrayed in *Grace & Frankie*. Your character was so aptly named—you personify the name. So tell me, you must *hear* all those silver ceilings breaking, right?

Your TED talk and passion for sharing your story strengthened my resolve to continue writing mine. Thank you. I cannot wait to finish reading *"Prime Time"* now that I have finished writing my book.

Ms. Lily Tomlin, I have revered and imitated you for almost my entire life, at least since I first saw you in your "Edith Anne" character on *Laugh-In* twenty-five years ago.

Thank you for your beautiful portrayal of Frankie Bergstein on *Grace & Frankie.* Your sensitivity, magical presence, and luminous sparkle warmed our hearts and made us howl with laughter, just as it did when you played Edith Anne, and that's the *truuuuuth!*

Dame Emma Thompson, I referred to you several times within these pages. I have even boldly referred to you as a *"Mirror, Mirror"* mentor. Women everywhere thank you from the bottom of our hearts (and bottoms!) for showing us your courage, self-love, and self-acceptance. You are magnificent. Lead on, goddess!

Ms. Iyanla Vanzant, you pack a serious punch, and I respect and admire you for that. Most of all, I thank you for that. Your compassion, strength, authenticity, and direct approach inspired me from the first time I saw you on *The Oprah Winfrey Show.*

Thank you for your wisdom. Your approach to forgiveness was an *"A-ha!"* moment that helped me recalibrate my life, and I will be forever grateful.

Ms. Arlene Dickinson, of all the podcasts I could have chosen during the pandemic, I decided to listen to your "Reinvention" program.

Like Bogie said, *"In all the gin joints in all the towns in all the world,"* your podcast came into my life when I needed it the most.

Thanks so much to you and your guests for the companionship and insights you provided during my walks through a very strange time indeed.

As a first-time author, I was inspired by your podcast and the personal reinventions you vulnerably shared in your book, *"Reinvention."* From one Canadian phoenix to another, thank you.

Ms. Lisa LaFlamme, after learning of your departure from CTV News, I felt compelled to return to my book draft and add a reference to your bravery. Please understand that I did not do this to embarrass you but to underscore that ageism is a real problem for women.

Ageism is mainly silent, and as a result, it regrettably slips under the radar as discriminatory behaviour.

Your unfortunate dismissal garnered outrage on an international scale. Your courage and vulnerability in sharing your story can catalyze change for all of us. Thank you.

Dr. Brené Brown, where does one start to say thank you to you and your work? You have taught us to explore and acknowledge our vulnerabilities and that it is safe to show all of who we are to the world. What a gift.

Thank you, Dr. Brown, for leading the way. You *are* a badass!

Sage Taylor Kingsley, thank you for your editorial guidance in writing my first book. You seemed to immediately "get" what and who I am about, and you understood and supported my vision. I am so grateful that our paths crossed and that you were such an integral part of this project. Thank you, Sage.

Candice Grandy	Rob Grandy
Scott Ackerman	Samantha Sutherland
Paula Richardson	Karen Schilbe
Jen Richardson	Suzanne Jackson
Lee Nash	Betsy Fleetwood
Billie Spooner	John Furanna
Cathie Hastings	

Thank you to all my pre- and post-editors, friends, and family whom I dragged into helping me edit and audit my musings. I am forever grateful for your feedback, candour, and time. *M'wah!*

Mom, I am looking at your artwork hanging on my office walls, and it serves as a beautiful reminder that it is never too late to start something new. You were in your 80s when you created your watercolour paintings, and you never realized how good they were.

Now these extraordinary paintings form part of your legacy, together with all the memories, love, and life lessons you gave us. You are forever in our hearts. We miss you. We thank you. We love you.

"IN MY LIFE" —The Beatles
I have had moments in my life that I treasure with people I love, some are still here and some have passed away. I cherish all the memories in my heart.

About the Author

Brenda is a full-fledged sexagenarian, and loving it!

renda took an early retirement from a ten-ured career with a Fortune 500 company where she started as a legal assistant and worked her way up to becoming an interna-tional multi-award-winning sales and marketing leader. Her work has been featured across North America at Guerilla Marketing Conferences, universities, and in publications.

She had the privilege of coaching and mentoring countless women (and men) through her career, and is extremely proud of being a part of their successful careers. She is hoping to coach and mentor once again, but this time by helping them navigate the aging process.

As a well-seasoned professional of her own life, after 60 years of practice, Brenda has developed superpowers that she could have never imagined. It is her sincere hope that, as you read this book, you will also find yourself in these pages because Brenda is most likely, very much like you.

Brenda is a proud mother of two wonderful adult children and a fantastic son-in-law. She is also an over-the-top grandmother to three beautiful grandchildren who call her "Dabba."

While enjoying her retirement, Brenda splits her time between Canada the United States, and she has many more travel and adventures planned for the future.